GET SET FO[...]
WEIRDEST V[...]

SENATOR J. E[...]WS'
FISCH – Unfortu[...]ly for the highly
moralistic senator, there were colour
photographs extant of a long-legged lady
with the senator's teeth-marks on her thigh.
In the hands of some dishonest politician,
these photos could halt some highly
profitable sidelines the senator had going
for him.

TAYLOR P. JAMBON – Gourmet, animal
lover and conman. He was founder and
executive director of APPLE (Association
of Pup and Pussy Lovers in Earnest, Inc.) –
and after operating expenses, there was
mighty little left over for the pups and
pussies.

LIEUTENANT JOANNE PAULINE
JONES – A remarkably well-stacked
blonde, she had joined the navy to see the
world. After her momentous trip as the first
skirted US navy officer ever to board a
nuclear submarine, she never quite saw
things the same way.

WEE BABY BROTHER – A schizophrenic
black Bengal tiger who thought he was a
puppy dog.

– PLUS OF COURSE, THE
HELL-RAISING MOB FROM M*A*S*H!

M*A*S*H
Goes To Vienna

**RICHARD HOOKER AND
WILLIAM E. BUTTERWORTH**

SPHERE BOOKS LIMITED
London and Sydney

First published in Great Britain
by Sphere Books Ltd 1979
30–32 Gray's Inn Road, London WC1X 8JL
Copyright © Richard Hornberger and
William E. Butterworth 1976
Reprinted 1979, 1984

Publisher's Note

This novel is a work of fiction. Names,
characters, places and incidents are either the
product of the author's imagination or are used
fictitiously, and any resemblance to actual
persons, living or dead, events, or locales is
entirely coincidental.

Filmset in Photon Times

Printed and bound in Great Britain by
Cox & Wyman Ltd, Reading

CHAPTER ONE

It was afternoon conference time in the office of the chief of surgery of the Spruce Harbor, Maine, Medical Center. The chief surgeon, Benjamin Franklin Pierce, M.D., F.A.C.S., was sitting, attired in somewhat mussed and sweat-soaked surgical greens, behind his desk. His bare and rather bony feet rested atop the tooled-Moroccan-leather desk pad on the desk; he sat slumped far enough down in his dark-red leather judge's chair so that a martini glass could rest (and indeed was resting) on his chest.

Two other practitioners of the cutting art were seated to Dr. Pierce's right on a two-seater leather couch. They too were attired in surgical greens, and they too had their feet off the ground and resting on a coffee table. The taller of the two, furthermore, also rested a martini glass on his chest. The shorter of the two had been denied, by the immutable idiosyncrasies of anatomy, the ability to rest a martini glass upon the upper portion of the body. She was Esther Flanagan, R.N., chief surgical nurse. It was necessary for her to hold her martini glass in a firm grip, its base resting on her tummy.

The taller of the two healers on the couch was John Francis Xavier McIntyre, M.D., F.A.C.S., and, like the others, he looked just a little worn and frazzled. It had been a busy day in the operating room, and while everything had eventually turned out well, everyone was quite aware that it very easily could have gone the other way and, in fact, with two patients almost had.

A fourth healer, sort of a journeyman cutter, Richard J. Wilson, M.D., officially described on the hospital roster as a surgical resident, was in the room. He was well aware of the social protocol involved. Participating in the postsurgical conference and critique was for him a privilege carrying with it both restrictions and obligations. He understood that it

7

would have been very bad form for him to have the effrontery to slump in a chair and put his unshod feet on a table. While he was quite welcome to partake of a libation or two, he understood further that not only was he expected to make the martinis for the others but to do so with painstaking care, lavishing at least as much attention on the precise gin-vermouth ratio, the temperature of the finished product, and the condition of the onions (three for Nurse Flanagan, two for Drs. McIntyre and Pierce) as he had ever lavished on any combination of chemicals and biologicals in a pharmacological laboratory.

And finally, he understood that his role was to be unseen and unheard. His role in the pecking order clearly denied him the privilege of loudly cheering on, with whistles and applause, as the others were, the painted savages with bones in their noses who were threatening Tarzan with their spears on 'The Movie Matinee,' which television extravaganza was being exhibited on the chief surgeon's bookcase-mounted apparatus.

Having ensured that Nurse Flanagan and Drs. Pierce and McIntyre were each equipped with a fresh, properly chilled martini, Dr. Wilson sat respectfully in a straight-backed chair and waited for the commercials. Unless it was a *good* commercial (a good commercial being one which afforded any of the trio the opportunity to reply to the unctuous ladies and gentlemen of the tube), there was frequently a medical comment or two to be offered. These comments were never directed to Dr. Wilson directly, but rather between the doctors and the lady. He was permitted, in other words, to eavesdrop on what he considered, not without reason, to be a top-notch critique of surgical procedures, and for this privilege he was perfectly willing to act as bartender and passer-of-the-peanuts. He had learned more about surgery from these three people in the last three months than he had learned in a year's formal training at a large and tactfully herein unnamed university medical centre.

He had also learned, as sort of a bonus, the opinions these three held of the other members of the medical staff of the Spruce Harbor Medical Center. This had been something of an education in itself, there being apparently little correlation between income and prestige and professional ability.

And when the telephone rang, Dr. Wilson knew his duty here, too. He leapt from his chair and grabbed the telephone before the first ring had died.

'Dr. Pierce,' he whispered, so as not to interfere with his superior's rapt fascination with Tarzan's plight, 'is in conference and not taking any calls.'

There was, in fact, a little button on Dr. Pierce's telephone which, when depressed, activated a signal light on the telephone switchboard, indicating that a conference was in progress and the telephone should not ring.

'Dr. Wilson looked at the television screen. It was commercial time. A wan-looking woman was staring soulfully at the camera.

'As a woman,' she said plaintively, 'I know I need more iron than a man. But how can I get it?'

'A nail a day,' Dr. John Francis Xavier McIntyre replied solemnly, 'keeps the doctor away.'

'Take two chocolate-flavoured carpet tacks before every meal,' Nurse Flanagan said, 'and again at bedtime.'

Dr. Pierce looked at Dr. Wilson.

'What did I do?' he asked. 'Forget to push that damned button again?'

'It's Mr. Crumley, Doctor,' Dr. Wilson replied.

T. Alfred Crumley, Sr., was not one of Dr. Pierce's favourite people in all the world, possibly because he was administrator of the Spruce Harbor Medical Center, and there were naturally some areas of potential strife and disagreement between the chief surgeon and the man in ultimate charge of the bedpans, parking lot and air-conditioning system.

On the other hand, Benjamin Franklin Pierce, M.D., was not one of T. Alfred Crumley, Sr.'s, favourite people either. Although his own medical career had faltered in the sophomore year of high school when Mr. Crumley, (then known to his peers as 'Elephant Ears' Crumley) had lost

9

consciousness and crashed to the floor during a frog dissection in Biology II, he still had very firm and positive ideas of the role and function of a physician and surgeon in society.

Both Dr. Pierce and Dr. McIntyre fell far short of Mr. Crumley's expectations. Not, it should be made instantly clear, insofar as their professional qualifications or skill was concerned. Even Elephant Ears had been known to admit that he considered the two of them (as indeed did their peers) to be about the best chest-cutters north of Boston and east of Chicago.

It was in their out-of-the-operating-room behaviour that Mr. Crumley felt improvement would be a good, even necessary thing. He did not think it lent dignity to the medical profession, for example, for a Fellow of the American College of Surgeons to arrive at his place of work attired in blue jeans, a T-shirt on which EAT MORE POSSUM had been imprinted in luminescent yellow paint, and at the wheel of a swamp buggy, as was Dr. McIntyre's custom.

Nor did he think it was at all conducive to the image of respectability of the medical profession generally and the professional staff of the Spruce Harbor Medical Center specifically for Dr. Pierce to go directly (and often in his surgical greens) from the operating room to the bar of the Bide-a-While Pool Hall/Ladies Served Fresh Lobster & Clams Daily Restaurant & Saloon, Inc., there to spend the balance of the afternoon in somewhat bawdy song with the proprietor, one Stanley K. Warczinski, Sr.

Mr. Crumley, furthermore, deeply suspected (although he could not prove) that in the near sacrosanct precincts of his office, Dr. Pierce actually provided spirituous liquors to certain privileged associates, while a locked door and a sign reading CONFERENCE IN SESSION gave the impression that he was about the hospital's business.

'Please tell Mr. Crumley,' Dr. Pierce said, sipping at his martini, 'that Dr. McIntyre and myself are in conference and do not wish to be disturbed.'

Dr. Wilson dutifully repeated this message to Mr. Crumley.

10

'I am quite sure I hear Applause,' Mr. Crumley said, somewhat sharply. 'Can you explain that?'

'Tarzan just fell out of a tree,' Dr. Wilson, who could not tell a lie, replied.

Dr. Pierce, having heard this, steadied his martini with his left hand and reached out for the telephone on his desk with his right.

'How they hanging, Crumley?' he asked.

'I trust I am not unnecessarily interrupting anything important?' Mr. Crumley asked.

'Get to the point, Crumley,' Dr. Pierce said. 'I'm a busy man.'

'You'll never guess who's here in our hospital,' T. Alfred Crumley said.

'I'm a little old for guessing games, Crumley,' Dr. Pierce said.

'Taylor P. Jambon!' T. Alfred Crumley announced, excitement in every quivering syllable. 'Himself!'

'You don't really mean that Taylor P. Jambon, the famous gourmet and animal lover himself, is really here in Spruce Harbor Medical Center!' Dr. Pierce replied. Without bothering to cover the mouthpiece, he addressed Dr. McIntyre: 'Trapper John, guess who's here in the hospital?'

'Taylor P. Jambon, the famous gourmet and animal lover himself,' Dr. McIntyre, who was also known as Trapper John,* replied.

'Thank you for the information, Mr. Crumley,' Dr. Pierce replied, 'but Dr. McIntyre, who keeps on top of things like this, already knew.'

'Mr. Jambon,' Mr. Crumley went on, 'came all the way here from Hollywood, California, to see Miss Patience Throckbottom Worthington.'

'You don't mean it!' Dr. Pierce said, and then again

---

*Dr. McIntyre, in his youth, had once been found in the Gentlemen's Rest Facility of a Boston & Bangor Railway car, somewhat *en déshabillé* and in the company of a University of Maine cheerleader. Although the young woman had in fact gone quite willingly with Dr. McIntyre, she had decided, in the interests of maintaining her good name, that it would be best if she told the conductor and the railway detective that she had been trapped. Hence, Trapper John.

11

addressed Dr. McIntyre. 'Mr. Jambon came all the way to see Miss Patience Throckbottom Worthington.'

'You don't mean it!' Trapper John said.

'I have it straight from Mr. Crumley himself,' Dr. Pierce replied. 'So it must be true.'

'Will wonders never cease?' Trapper John said.

'And there seems to be some little mix-up,' Mr. Crumley went on.

'Is that so?' Dr. Pierce replied.

'There is a "Positively No Admission, Positively No Visitors" sign on Miss Worthington's door,' Mr. Crumley said.

'You don't say?'

'It bears your signature,' Mr. Crumley said.

'So it does,' Dr. Pierce admitted.

'Far be it from me, as hospital administrator, to even suggest to question a medical decision of one of the professional staff, much less our distinguished chief of surgery,' Mr. Crumley went on, 'but according to the records, Miss Worthington is suffering from a fractured right femur and a fractured left humerus.'*

'Known in the trade as a busted leg and a busted arm,' Dr. Pierce replied. 'Your information is correct, Mr. Crumley. That sometimes happens when you take one giant step from an airliner door to the ground.'

'So far as I know,' Mr. Crumley went on, 'broken limbs

---

*Miss Patience Throckbottom Worthington, star of stage, screen and lately television, had come to Maine for the on-location filming of the first episode of the Wesley St. James television daytime drama series 'The Code of the Deep Woods,' in which she was to play the role of kindly Grandmother Nobleheart. There were some problems, including Miss Worthington's condition when she arrived at Spruce Harbor International Airport full of good cheer, specifically Old White Stagg Blended Kentucky Bourbon, and exited the aircraft without benefit of stairs.

The series had to be cancelled, of course, and the production crew left, leaving Miss Worthington in the Spruce Harbor Medical Center. The details of this affair have been recorded in somewhat revolting detail in the otherwise highly literate and culturally enriching tome *M*A*S*H Goes to Hollywood* also in Sphere Books which is offered for sale in bus and airline terminals, drugstores, five-and-ten-cent stores and other gathering places for literary cognoscenti.

are not contagious, and Miss Worthington's latest charts indicate she is recuperating as well as can be expected, under the circumstances.'

'Right you are,' Dr. Pierce replied.

'May I then inquire why it is your medical judgment that the patient's best interests will be served by medical isolation?' Crumley asked.

'It has nothing to do with the patient's best interests,' Dr. Pierce said.

'I don't follow you, Doctor.'

'I told Miss Worthington that the next time she drove one of our teenaged hospital helpers, one of our candy-stripers, to tears by referring to the food she was served as a bleeping pile of blap served by a bleeping blap, I would throw her in the slammer. She did, and I did.'

'There must be some misunderstanding!' Mr. Crumley protested.

'No, none at all,' Dr. Pierce replied. 'I heard her myself. I haven't heard such language since I was a military surgeon in Korea and the walls of the nurses' shower somehow came tumbling down while Major Hot Lips Houlihan was performing her ablutions.'

'It made me blush,' Trapper John said.

'Dr. McIntyre said it made *him* blush,' Dr. Pierce went on. 'So there you are!'

'But Mr. Taylor P. Jambon has come all the way from Hollywood, California, to see Miss Worthington,' Mr. Crumley said.

'Hawkeye,' Trapper John said, 'I have just had a thought.'

'Hold everything, Crumbum,' Dr. Pierce said. 'Dr. McIntyre is thinking.'

'That's Crumley, Dr. Pierce,' Mr. Crumley said, somewhat icily.

'Hawkeye, I would say,' Trapper John said, 'that Miss Worthington and Mr. Taylor P. Jambon deserve each other. How 'bout that, Flanagan?'

'He's got something, Hawkeye,' Esther Flanagan said, rising with some effort from the couch to steady her martini glass as Dr. Wilson refilled it.

13

'O.K., Crumley,' Hawkeye said, 'you have my permission to let him in for thirty minutes.'

'Thank you very much,' Mr. Crumley said, and the phone went dead.

Dr. Hawkeye Pierce laid the telephone back in its cradle and returned his attention to the television.

'Oh, damn,' he said, with genuine regret. 'I should have known that the good guys could never win. Here comes that damned elephant again to save Tarzan.'

'Disgusting, that's what it is,' Nurse Flanagan said. She raised her head to look at Dr. Wilson. 'Turn it off, Junior,' she ordered.

'I read somewhere,' Trapper John said, 'that too much martini drinking in the afternoon is bad for you. What do you say we all go down to the Bide-a-While for a beer?'

'Good thinking, Trapper John,' Hawkeye Pierce said. 'This hospital is not big enough for Taylor P. Jambon and me at the same time.'

Dr. Wilson quickly began to clear away the glasses, peanuts, and booze bottles. Dr. McIntyre called the Recovery Room, got favourable reports from the nurse on duty concerning their patients, and then called the switchboard.

'This is Dr. McIntyre,' he said. 'Dr. Pierce, Dr. Wilson, Nurse Flanagan and I will be in the laboratory. Will you please adjust the Professional Personnel Locator Board accordingly?'

That accomplished, Dr. McIntyre stepped to the curtains covering the windows of the office. He drew them back. Dr. Pierce opened the window and then bowed Nurse Flanagan through. The nurse waited on the lawn beside the long-needled pine and other evergreens until the doctors had joined her. Then, arm in arm, they marched across the lawn to the swamp buggy, climbed aboard, and with a roar of the diesel engine and a cloud of blue smoke, departed the grounds of the Spruce Harbor Medical Center for the Bide-a-While Pool Hall.*

* It would not do, of course, to have the Professional Personnel Locator Board (more popularly known as the Doctor Board), which was on prominent display in the hospital lobby, publicly announce that one or

They had gone but fifty or seventy yards when the air was rent with a bloodcurdling scream, a piteous wail of abject horror. The swamp buggy skidded through a U-turn, raced up to the main entrance and skidded to a halt. Its passengers leaped down from it and raced inside the hospital.

---

more healers were hoisting a beer in the Bide-a-While Pool Hall, or even chasing a small white ball around the grassy expanse of the Spruce Harbor Country Club. Certain euphemisms were employed: the Country Club was known on the Doctor Board as 'The Board of Health,' for example, and 'Board Meeting' meant that the follower of Hippocrates had been in the office of the chief of surgery and was more than likely in no condition whatever to practise any kind of medicine requiring sober judgment. 'The Laboratory,' of course, was the bar of the Bide-a-While Pool Hall/Ladies Served Fresh Lobster & Clams Daily Restaurant and Saloon, Inc.

CHAPTER TWO

Taylor P. Jambon, famous television gourmet and animal lover, had indeed journeyed all the way across the country from Hollywood, California, to Spruce Harbor, Maine, to see America's most beloved actress, Patience Throckbottom Worthington, in (or on) her bed of pain. But, there was a certain element of enlightened self-interest in the sage's journey. His journey was not, as he announced on his show, 'a humble homage to kneel at the feet of America's most beloved thespians.' (He pronounced humble homage 'umble omage,' as a good Harvard man should.)

As he confided to his crony and silent partner, Senator J. Ellwood 'Jaws' Fisch (Moralist-Liberal, Calif.), there were few things in all the world which would get him out of Beverly Hills, California, and off to Spruce Harbor, Maine, the very plebeian syllables of which were an affront to the ears of a refined sybarite and arbiter of good taste such as himself.

'The cold truth of the matter, Jaws . . .' he said.

'I've told you before, and I'll tell you again, Taylor P.,' the senator replied, 'I would rather that you didn't call me "Jaws".'

'That's what that "model" called you when you bit her on the thigh,' Taylor P. Jambon said. 'And with good reason, according to the photographs I saw.'

'How did you get to see the photographs?' the senator inquired.

'Who do you think bought them from the photographer? Santa Claus? Sometimes, Jaws, your naiveté beggars description. I'd hate to tell you what they cost APPLE*!' He paused and then went on righteously: 'No, I think you *should* know.' He told him.

---

*APPLE is the popular acronym for the Association of Pup and Pussy Lovers in Earnest, Inc., which body Mr. Jambon had founded and in which he served as executive director.

'*That* much?' the senator asked, with mingled doubt and pride.

'It isn't every day that the newspapers of this country are given a chance to run a front-page picture of some long-legged female with a senator's teeth marks on her thigh,' Taylor P. Jambon said. 'Think about it.'

'But you fixed it? The pictures have been destroyed?'

'Let's say they are out of circulation,' Taylor P. Jambon said. 'The photographer, too. He has retired to a sunny Greek island. He bought it with what I gave him for the pictures.'

'Well, APPLE's got the money,' the senator said, practically. 'What's the difference?'

'Before you so rudely interrupted me,' Taylor P. Jambon said, 'I was going to bring that up.'

'Get to the point, Taylor P.,' the senator said. He was getting a little bored with all this. He had a busy day planned. First a luncheon meeting in the Beverly Wilshire Hotel, during which he would give stock speech B-2, 'Television Is Ruining Our Children's Morals,' and following which he was returning to Washington, D.C., aboard an Air Force Sabreliner provided by the grateful taxpayers and in company of a young woman who had told him she would 'do anything to get into government.' The senator was looking forward to plumbing the depths of the young woman's dedication.

'I'm afraid of you, Jaws,' Taylor P. Jambon said. 'That's the bottom line.'

'You're afraid of *me*? You know full well, Taylor, that I am a sworn foe of violence of any kind. That includes fistfighting.'

'I'm not talking about fistfighting, you cretin. I'm talking about your public image!'

Senator Fisch examined himself in the mirror. He found nothing wrong with his bushy eyebrows, his prominent cheekbones, and the full set of flashing, gleaming choppers which had given him the 'Jaws' nickname, even before the unfortunate incident with the nibbled thigh.

'What's wrong with my public image?'

'When the TV stations run our APPLE Crusade spots, I

17

want all the folks out there in TV-land to have mental images of starving pups and starving pussycats, not a mental picture of you taking a bite out of some bimbo's upper leg.'

'You really know how to hurt a guy, don't you, Taylor P. Jambon?' the senator replied, somewhat plaintively.

'Of course, I do,' Taylor P. replied. 'There's no place on the professional gourmet circuit for sissies.'

'Huh!' The senator snorted deprecatingly. 'Don't try to hand me that. I'm a U.S. senator, you know.'

'I don't mean that kind of sissy, you idiot,' Taylor P. said.

'Oh,' the senator replied. 'So what's on your mind?'

'Patience Throckbottom Worthington,' Taylor P. Jambon said, pronouncing each syllable very carefully.

'Jesus, Taylor P., sometimes you're really wierd! She's old enough to be my mother. She's old enough to be *your* mother!'

'Get your mind out of the gutter, Jaws, and listen to me,' Taylor P. Jambon said. 'I'll take it from the top.'

'I'm all ears,' the senator said.

'We've got a good thing going with APPLE,' Taylor P. Jambon said. 'If we don't drop the ball, it'll go on forever. There's always going to be puppies and pussycats. No smart ass is going to come up with a cure for that. Look what happened to the March of Dimes. Everything was going along great, all peaches and cream, and then, out of the blue, some wise guy in a white jacket jerks the whole disease out from under them. They had to do some fast and fancy footwork to find some other disease, or the whole thing was over.'

'I still don't know what this has got to do with Patience Throckbottom Worthington,' the senator said.

'I'm going to use her instead of you, Jaws, for the commercials,' Taylor P. Jambon said. He said this as a flat statement of fact. It wasn't a suggestion; it was an announcement.

'Now, wait just a minute,' the senator said. 'Me doing those commercials was part of the deal.'

'Before you bit the broad it was part of the deal,' Taylor P. said. 'It's a whole new ball game now, Jaws.'

18

'People see me up there on the tube, begging money for pussycats and puppy dogs, and they vote for me,' the senator said. 'It makes them think of me as a kindly father figure, concerned about their problems.'

'You should have thought about that before you tried to eat that dame's leg,' Taylor P. Jambon said.

'We all make mistakes,' the senator said. 'Even you make mistakes, Taylor. You're the guy who told his viewers to marinate roast beef in gin. That set kitchens on fire from coast to coast.'

'Be that as it may,' Taylor P. Jambon, stung to the quick, said.

'What about Rice Pilaf à la Jambon? You said two quarts instead of two cups, and you had rice running all over the floor of two hundred thousand kitchens.'

'Shut up, Jaws,' Taylor P. Jambon said. 'That's neither here nor there.'

'If you think I'm going to give up making those commercials, getting on television screens all over the country two and three times a day, on prime time, you've got another think coming, Taylor P. Jambon.'

'I've already had my other think. Patience Throckbottom Worthington does the commercials.'

'Or?'

'Or Mrs. Fisch gets full-colour eleven-by-fourteen-inch prints of the bimbo's leg, Jaws,' Taylor P. Jambon said. 'Purple teeth marks and all.'

'On reflection,' the senator intoned, 'perhaps you have something, Taylor P.'

'That's better,' Taylor P. Jambon replied. 'Now, nothing is really going to be changed much if you keep your cool. You keep Congress of my back, and APPLE will keep you on the payroll as a consultant.'

'If I'm not going to get to go on television with the APPLE Crusade commercials, I think we had better re-negotiate my consultant fee. Fifty thousand a year isn't fair compensation for the consulting services of a U.S. senator, Taylor P., and you know it.'

'You still own thirty-five per cent of the Pup and Pussy

19

Hospitals,* Jaws,' Taylor P. Jambon said. 'You're forgetting that.'

'*I* know that,' the senator replied. 'But what I'm worried about is Patience Throckbottom Worthington. What's she going to cost us?'

'A lot less now than before,' Taylor P. Jambon replied confidently.

'What's that supposed to mean?'

'She fell off an airplane in Maine and broke her leg,' Taylor P. said. 'That means she's out of a job. We can get her for peanuts.'

'How many peanuts?' the senator pursued.

'Look at it this way, Jaws,' Taylor P. Jambon said. 'The old bag is regarded by most of the idiots who send us money as really something special. For thirty years, who has done *The Night Before Christmas* bit on the tube on Christmas Eve? Patience Throckbottom Worthington, that's who.'

'What's that got to do with us?'

'She's everybody's saintly grandmother, Jaws. When she starts talking about starving pups and pussycats, there won't be a dry eye in America. And, oh, how the money'll roll in!'

'You really think so?' the senator asked.

'Trust me, Jaws,' Taylor P. Jambon said. 'Don't worry your pretty head about it. You just make sure some damned honest politician doesn't start snooping around.'

'Not to worry,' Senator 'Jaws' Fisch said. 'They're all too busy investigating each other.'

'See that it stays that way,' Taylor P. Jambon said, 'and we're home free. In six months, no one will even remember what that broad said about you.'

And so, steeling himself for the journey into the hinterlands with a half pound of beluga caviar washed down with a

---

* One of the many good works of APPLE was the free spaying service. Pet owners could bring their dogs and cats to any of the eleven Pup and Pussy Hospitals for the procedure, absolutely free of charge. On a production-line schedule, the procedure cost the Pup and Pussy Hospitals $2.75 per animal. They were compensated for this service by APPLE at $7.50 per operation, for a net profit of $4.75 per operation. The Pup and Pussy Hospitals were operated by a Mr. Homer Walton, who happened to be Mr. Taylor P. Jambon's brother-in-law.

jeroboam of Piper Heidsieck '51, Taylor P. Jambon left his Beverly Hills, California, *pied-à-terre* and headed for Spruce Harbor, Maine.

It was a ghastly trip. Some incompetent in the public-relations department of the airline had screwed things up. There was a complimentary seat in the first-class compartment of the plane, of course, but just one seat, when the airline should have known full well that trying to squeeze Taylor P. Jambon's hind quarters into just one seat was like trying to squeeze toothpaste back in the tube. Even worse than that, the necessary orders had not been issued to the airline's commissary department, and at chow time Mr. Jambon was forced to partake of the same barbarous slop (fillet mignon, baked potato, cherries jubilee and *café royale*) served to the other first-class passengers. (Mr. Jambon didn't even like to *think* about what the peasants back in the tourist class were being fed.)

And when he arrived at Spruce Harbor Medical Center, he was bluntly informed that Miss Worthington was in medical isolation and could not receive visitors.

'My dear young woman,' he had said, 'I am Taylor P. Jambon!'

She had stared at him with mild curiosity.

'The famous gourmet and animal lover,' he went on. Incredibly, she had never heard of him, and worse, said so.

'Certainly,' he had said, just a shade hysterical, 'there must be someone, even in this domestic Siberia, with a modicum of culture and refinement, who will understand that when Taylor P. Jambon wishes to visit America's most beloved thespian, Taylor P. Jambon gets to visit America's most beloved thespian.'

'I think you're wrong about that, pal,' the receptionist said.

'Wrong about what?'

'She likes men. Oh, boy, does she like men! We have to send the ward boys in there in pairs. For their own safety. Even hung-up the way she is.'

At that point, fortunately, confirming Taylor P. Jambon's long-held belief that there was a divine purpose to his life, the hospital administrator, one T. Alfred Crumley, happened to pass through the hospital lobby, past the receptionist's station.

'Oh, my!' Mr. Crumley had said, clapping his hands together in something like ecstasy. 'Can it *really* be Taylor P. Jambon, America's most famous gourmet and animal lover, here in *my* little hospital?'

'Indeed it is,' Mr. Jambon replied. 'And who, sir, are you?'

'I am T. Alfred Crumley, Sr., administrator of the Spruce Harbor Medical Center. And how may I be of service, Mr. Jambon?'

'I have come to pay 'umble 'omage at the feet of Miss Patience Throckbottom Worthington,' Taylor P. Jambon said.

'How utterly *gracious* of you!' Mr. T. Alfred Crumley, Sr., replied. He turned to the receptionist. 'What is Miss Worthington's room number?'

'Not a chance, Crumbum,' the receptionist said.

'What do you mean, "not a chance"?' Mr. Crumley snapped. 'And that's *Mr.* Crumbum. I mean, *Mr.* Crum-*ley.*'

'Hawkeye says no visitors,' the receptionist said. 'And no deliveries of food, booze, or anything else. And when Hawkeye says no visitors, food, booze, or anything else, he means no . . .'

'And where is Dr. Pierce at this time?' Mr. Crumley replied, shutting her off.

'In conference. And you know that when Hawkeye's in conference, he doesn't like to be disturbed,' the receptionist said, adding, *sotto voce*, 'Especially by you, Crumbum.'

Mr. Crumley looked a trifle disturbed for a moment. Then he straightened his shoulders.

'Mr. Jambon,' he said, 'I'm sure that an exception can be made in your case. If you would be good enough to come to my office with me, I will speak with Dr. Pierce on the telephone. And while we're there, perhaps you would be good enough to autograph my copy of *The Taylor P. Jambon Gourmet Guide to Gustatory Goodies*?'

'For you, Mr. Crumbum,' Taylor P. Jambon replied, grandly, 'without charge.'

22

Five minutes later, Mr. Taylor P. Jambon gently pushed open the door to the hospital room of Miss Patience Throckbottom Worthington. He withdrew it quickly, and just in time to avoid a stainless-steel bedpan which came flying through the air. It hit the door and crashed to the floor.

'Miss Worthington,' he cried, 'it is I, Taylor P. Jambon!'

'How dare you, you bleeping creep, walk into *my* room without so much as a bleeping knock?' Miss Patience Throckbottom Worthington, America's most beloved thespian, screamed.

'Dear lady,' Mr. Jambon replied from behind the safety of the heavy hospital door, 'there is apparently some slight misunderstanding. It is I, Taylor P. Jambon, famous gourmet and animal lover, come to pay 'umble 'omage at your feet.'

'Then why the bleep didn't you say so, you bleeping ignoramus?' Miss Worthington asked. 'I don't suppose you've got a little snort with you, do you?'

'As it happens, dear lady,' Taylor P. Jambon said, reaching into the breast pocket of his chartreuse sports coat and coming up with a silver flask. He extended the flask beyond the edge of the door so that it could be seen. 'I do happen to have some spirits with me. In case of emergency, of course.'

'If this isn't a bleeping emergency, I don't know what one is,' Miss Worthington said. 'You may enter.'

Taylor P. Jambon entered the room and walked up to the bed. America's most beloved thespian was in a hospital bed, the back of which had been cranked up. Her right leg was in a cast from the ankle to the groin and her left arm in a cast from the wrist to the shoulder.

'Dear lady!' he said. 'What have they done to you?'

'What the bleep does it look like, you bleeping jackass?' Miss Worthington replied. 'They've got me in a bleeping cast from my ankle to my* (———). Not to mention what the blaps did to my bleeping arm. Hand me that bleeping flask, will you, Fatso?'

---

*(Miss Worthington here used a somewhat scatological term for a portion of her anatomy which has no place in a morally uplifting tome like this one and has been deleted.)

23

Mr. Taylor P. Jambon handed over the flask. Miss Worthington took it with her good arm, removed the cork with her teeth, spit the cork out, and then tipped the flask up to her lips. She drank half of its contents with a steady gurgle-gurgle, finally removed it from her lips, belched mightily and looked at Mr. Taylor P. Jambon.

'Never look a gift horse in the face, I always say,' she said. 'What's on your bleeping mind, Fatso?'

'I came, dear lady,' Taylor P. Jambon said, 'the moment I heard of your tragic accident.'

'Stop right there, Fatso,' Miss Worthington said. 'It wasn't a bleeping accident. It was a bleeping assassination* attempt, and I know which bleeping blap was responsible for it. The minute I can get out of this bleeping bed . . .'

'Wesley St. James is an evil man . . .' Mr. Taylor P. Jambon said, making a guess. He had done very well in his career making wild guesses.

'You bet your blap he's an evil man,' Miss Worthington said. She looked closer at Taylor P. Jambon. 'I didn't catch the name, Fatso.'

'I am Taylor P. Jambon,' he said modestly.

'Never heard of you,' Miss Worthington replied. 'But a friend in need is a friend indeed, as I always say.' She extended his flask to him. 'Have a little snort, Jawbone.'

'Jambon, Miss Worthington,' he corrected her.

'Whatever,' she said. 'Save some for me. You wouldn't believe how dry it's been in here. What's on your mind, Jawbone?'

'Miss Worthington,' Taylor P. Jambon said, 'in addition to being the famous television gourmet, I am the founder and executive director of APPLE.'

* Miss Worthington believed that the stewardess of the aircraft from which she fell was fully aware, when she advised Miss Worthington to 'watch her step,' that no portable stairway had been pushed against the aircraft door and that the step Miss Worthington took without looking was thirty-two feet straight down. Further, she had somehow gotten the idea that Mr. Wesley St. James, the producer of the television series in which she was to star, was responsible. Both Mr. St. James and the stewardess involved invoked the Fifth Amendment to the Constitution when questioned by police.

24

'You don't say?' Miss Worthington said, sitting up with a grunt to snatch the flask from his hand.

'You know, of course, about APPLE and the APPLE Crusade?' Mr. Jambon pursued.

'Not the first bleeping thing,' Miss Worthington confessed. "If you're some kind of a bleeping evangelist, Jawbone, I think I should tell you you're wasting your time in here.'

'APPLE is the acronym for the Association of Pup and Pussy Lovers in Earnest,' Taylor P. Jambon said.

'You're kidding,' Miss Worthington said. 'Well, what's that got to do with me? I can't stand bleeping animals of any bleeping variety.'

'Not even puppy dogs and pussycats?' Taylor P. said, disappointment in his voice.

'*Especially* puppy dogs and pussycats,' Miss Worthington replied. 'They give me the bleeping hives.'

'I understand the allergists can do wonders these days,' Mr. Taylor P. Jambon said. 'Dear lady, if you would be good enough to give me a few minutes of your precious time, I have a business proposition I would like to make to you.'

'I was afraid it would be a *business* proposition,' Miss Worthington said, somewhat sadly. 'You smell like a Parisian pansy. But what the bleep? At least you brought a jug. Let's hear your bleeping proposition.'

CHAPTER THREE

Six months previously, Brigadier Montague Fyffe (Royal Army, Retired), chief of staff of Folkestone Castle, Ltd., and as such in charge of the Folkestone Castle Zoo (Admission two Shillings, Children Under Twelve Half-price) watched with genuine regret (and, if the truth be known, tears in his eyes) as a veterinarian laboured long and hard and fruitlessly in an attempt to save the life of Princess, a black Bengal tigress who had experienced fatal complications while delivering two cubs, one of which was born dead.

Finally, the veterinarian had gotten off his knees and turned to face Brigadier Fyffe.

'She's gone, I'm afraid,' he said. 'God knows, I did everything I know how to do.'

'And the cub?' Brigadier Fyffe, oblivious to the damage he was doing to his rather elegant suit, picked up the small, wet black bundle of newborn life and cradled it tenderly against him.

'So far as I can tell,' the veterinarian said, 'it's healthy. I'll leave a formula with the cat keeper, and you can try to keep it alive. Keep it warm, try to get it to eat, and we'll see.'

'You don't really hold out much hope, do you, Doctor?' Brigadier Fyffe asked.

'It's hard enough to raise cubs in captivity when the mother's around,' the veterinarian said. 'Now . . .'

'Such a pity,' Brigadier Fyffe said. 'I had such high hopes. Black Bengal tigers are so rare. And we tried so hard.'

'I'm sorry, Brigadier,' the veterinarian said.

'I must,' the brigadier said as much to himself as to the doctor, 'bear these sad tidings to Her Grace.'

He straightened his shoulders, flexed his moustache and marched erectly out of the Cat House. (For some reason, the 75,000 or so American tourists who visited Folkestone Castle, Ltd., annually reacted rather oddly to the perfectly innocuous and certainly quite simple nomenclature. The brigadier understood, of course, why the blue-haired-lady element among the guests might tend to be disappointed to learn upon entering that the cats were behind bars, weighed several hundred pounds, and frankly had a certain odour. But why veritable hordes of American men should practically rush the premises, beaming from ear to ear, only to emerge moments later downcast and/or furious, muttering about deceptive British advertising, he didn't pretend to understand.)

He climbed aboard his in-grounds transport vehicle, unfurled the flags, and switched on the radio.

'Control,' he said, sharply, 'chief of staff from the Cat House to the Castle.'

He then engaged the clutch and moved swiftly and smoothly out of the zoo itself, through the Folkestone Castle Game Park, past the Duke's Taproom Number Six, the Ducal Roller Coaster, the Bus & Van Parking Lot and up the footpath leading to Folkestone Castle itself. He rolled across the bridge over the moat, drove across the courtyard and stopped the in-grounds transport vehicle before the private entrance to the castle. He saw the black Rolls-Royce Silver Shadow saloon motorcar of Mr. Angus MacKenzie, V.C., parked in the space which a discreet sign emblazoned with the Folkestone coat of arms announced was 'RESERVED FOR HER GRACE.'

Her Grace was the dowager duchess of Folkestone, formerly Miss Florabelle Jenkins, who had been executive castlekeeper of Folkestone Castle Properties, Ltd., until the previous year. Following the untimely death, at ninety-four,* of Vice Admiral Lord Hugh Percival, the Duke of Folkestone, at that time, the announcement in His Grace's last will and testament that Miss Jenkins had been the fruit of a somewhat clandestine union between himself and a Mrs. Ernestine Jenkins, had both caused something of a stir among the upper aristocracy and seen Miss Jenkins assume, rather belatedly, her rightful title.

---

* The Duke expired of coronary failure while being pursued through Hyde Park by Lieutenant General Sir Archibald Sommersby (Royal Army, Retired), aged eighty-eight, who, armed with a shotgun, was attempting to

Mr. Angus MacKenzie (Royal Marines, Retired), a long-time friend of Miss Jenkins, had also been the boon companion of the late duke. There had been some raised eyebrows when, shortly after the demise of the duke and the elevation of Miss Jenkins to dowager duchess, the two announced their marriage. Some spoilsports said that it was absolutely unfitting for the dowager duchess of Folkestone to marry someone who, in thirty years in the Royal Marines, had never risen above the enlisted rank of company sergeant major. It was suggested that Mr. MacKenzie (often described as the 'awful Scotsman') had married the dowager duchess for her money.

Mr. MacKenzie's defenders, and there were many, including Brigadier Fyffe, pointed out that Mr. MacKenzie had been for years managing director of East Anglia Breweries, Ltd., one of the late duke's many commercial holdings and had received all of the stock of the breweries as a bequest in the duke's last will and testament. He didn't need the dowager duchess' money.

Mr. MacKenzie, furthermore, had enjoyed the full trust and confidence of the duke during the last thirty years of the duke's long life, an association which had begun when Mr. MacKenzie, then Marine orderly to Vice Admiral His Grace the Duke of Folkestone, had earned the Victoria Cross for keeping His Grace afloat and alive when HMS *Indefatigable* (of which the duke had been captain) had been torpedoed and sunk in the opening days of World War II.

Truth to tell, however, it had been at first difficult for Brigadier Fyffe, and others of his ilk, to accept Mr. MacKenzie as the consort. One simply was taken a bit aback at the spectacle of a dowager duchess and a former Royal Marine company sergeant major walking hand in hand

---

shoot His Grace, whom he had discovered *in flagrante delicto* with Lady Sommersby, aged sixty-four, in the duke's apartment in the Dorchester Hotel. The details of this affair, for those interested in the fine points of noble accession and/or of hanky-panky among the hoi polloi, are available in the scholarly tome *M*A*S*H Goes to London* also in Sphere Books, which is generally to be found offered for sale on the better paperback bookracks, at a very nominal price indeed.

through the castle grounds, billing and cooing like a pair of fourteen-year-olds, addressing one another as 'Dumpling' and 'Snookums' and taking frequent pulls from the neck of a quart bottle of Royal Highland Dew Straight Scots Whisky.

And then there were the dogs. Mr. MacKenzie had been known throughout his long Royal Marine Corps career as 'Black Dog' MacKenzie. This did not make reference, as some alleged, to his being a black-hearted Scotsman but rather to the fact that he had rarely been, since his days as a Marine guard at Governor General's House, New Delhi, without the company of a canine companion.

His first dog (known, as were all the others, simply as 'Wee Black Doggie') had been an Indian mongrel of unknown pedigree. He had acquired it while on guard duty, a small, black starving puppy who had followed him on his rounds around the Governor General's Rose Garden. Then Private First-class MacKenzie had taken the puppy back with him to Marine barracks, bathed it, wormed it, and watched it with delight as the small, ungainly pup grew to maturity.

At maturity, the first Wee Black Doggie stood three-and-a-half feet at the shoulders and weighed just under ten stone.* He went down with HMS *Indefatigable*, having given his all for Crown and Country. A photograph of him hangs in a place of honour (above the bar) in the Sword, Crown & Anchor Hotel, traditional off-duty gathering place of the Royal Marine Corps in London.

As soon as he was able to do so (after he got out of the hospital, a year later) Vice Admiral His Grace the Duke of Folkestone had naturally considered it his duty as an officer and a gentleman to replace the animal his orderly (and saviour) had lost in the sinking of HMS *Indefatigable*. Since it was impossible at the time to scour the alleys of New Delhi for a replacement mongrel of suitable size and colour, His Grace did the next best thing. He scoured the Scottish

---

* A stone is the rather interesting (some say odd) manner in which the English describe the weight of a man or a large animal. One stone is fourteen pounds. The first Wee Black Doggie, thus, weighed approximately one hundred forty pounds.

Highlands for the largest, meanest Scottish wolfhound he could find. (Most canine geneticists believe the Scottish wolfhound is a cross between the Irish wolfhound and the wolf. It is, in any event, the only animal from which the Irish wolfhound will invariably flee in absolute terror.)

When the duke presented the replacement animal (then just a five-month-old pup weighing hardly over six stone (or eighty-four pounds), it had been appropriate, of course, to raise a wee cup in the memory of their comrades-in-arms (including, of course, Wee Black Doggie) who had gone down with HMS *Indefatigable*. One wee cup led to another. The duke and the sergeant major came to realize that they, despite the vast difference in social position, were, so to speak, birds of a feather. Three days later, when the ducal Rolls-Royce bounced back down the rocky mountain trail from the MacKenzie cottage, Angus MacKenzie and Wee Black Doggie were in the back seat.

Two weeks later, Mr. Angus MacKenzie, V.C., *The Brewer's Gazette* reported, had been unanimously elected general manager of East Anglia Breweries, Ltd., following the resignation 'for personal reasons' of the incumbent, Vice Admiral His Grace the Duke of Folkestone. The vote was unanimous because the duke owned all the stock.

For the next thirty years, the two retired gentlemen were practically inseparable. There was grouse shooting in the highlands, deerstalking on the moors, and, it was none too discreetly bandied about, the pursuit of certain two-legged short-skirted French game in Monte Carlo and other such watering places.

They were always accompanied by Wee Black Doggie. Not always the same Wee Black Doggie, of course, because the Grim Canine Reaper took his regular toll, but always a Wee Black Doggie and sometimes as many as two or three Wee Black Doggies at once. At full growth, Wee Black Doggies generally stood about four feet at the shoulder and weighed somewhere in the neighbourhood of twenty to twenty-two stone (280–308 pounds), stretching, nose to tail, anywhere from eight to ten feet.

Wee Black Doggie was always a boy Wee Black Doggie,

the idea of having a girl Wee Black Doggie never having really entered the mind of Mr. MacKenzie, and certainly not that of His Grace, at all.

Marriage, as the reader may him or herself have noticed, frequently changes long-standing, even sacrosanct tradition. Such it was with the gender of Wee Black Doggie.

Immediately following his marriage, Mr. MacKenzie found himself, for the first time in forty years, without a Wee Black Doggie. The incumbent had been presented, in a moment's emotional weakness, to a Miss Beverly Chambers, a young American friend of the new Duke of Folkestone.*

He did not notice the absence of a canine companion immediately, it must be reported. He had been married three whole days before he woke with a start to realize that the body against which he was warming his feet was not covered with heavy black fur but rather nylon lace.

'My God!' he cried, sitting up in bed. 'Wee Black Doggie!'

'Snookums gave him to Woody's sweet little friend,' the

---

* On the death of Vice Admiral His Grace the Duke of Folkestone, the title passed to his grand-nephew the Honorable Hugh Percival Woodburn-Haverstraw, then serving as a midshipman aboard HMS *Insubmergible*. The subtle nuances of the situation may be found explored with some skill and finesse, and at great length, in *M*A*S*H Goes to London*, and it will suffice to note here simply that His Grace then eighteen years old, had become rather friendly with Miss Chambers, also then eighteen years old, while he was a patient in the Spruce Harbor (Maine) Medical Center. At the suggestion of B. F. Pierce, M.D., who with Miss Chambers medically attended His Grace during the internment rites of the late Duke in London, and with, of course, Her Majesty's permission, Midshipman His Grace the Duke of Folkestone was appointed to the United States Naval Academy, at Annapolis, Maryland, by Congressman Edwards L. 'Smiling Jack' Jackson (Farmer-Free Silver, Ark.) and Congressman Anthony J. 'Tiny Tony' Pasquale (Liberal-Republican, N.J.) in exchange for Dr. Pierce's promise that he would not release certain photographs of the distinguished solons that he had in his possession to the press.

At the suggestion of Her Grace the Dowager Duchess of Folkestone, Mr. Angus MacKenzie presented Wee Black Doggie to Miss Chambers to keep her company while His Grace was at Annapolis. Mr. MacKenzie's unexpected generosity in this may be fairly attributed to three things. He had just married the dowager duchess; Miss Chambers was the second female in his memory (the first being the dowager duchess) whom Wee Black Doggie had not tried to eat; and thirdly, he was rather in his cups at the time.

dowager duchess, sitting up herself, replied. 'Has Snookums forgotten?'

'Of course not, Dumpling,' Mr. MacKenzie replied, not entirely truthfully. 'I was under the impression, however, that it was more in the nature of a loan than a gift.'

'It was not,' the dowager duchess said. 'You *gave* that sweet child that animal, Angus MacKenzie, and don't try to worm out of it.' She paused and wilted at the sight of his face. Tragedy was written all over its somewhat ruddy and worn contours. 'Snookums,' she said, 'you can always get another.'

'Right you are, Dumpling,' MacKenzie had replied, swinging his feet out of bed. 'I'll be back the day after tomorrow. Behave yerself while I'm away.'

'You're leaving our . . . nuptial couch . . . on the third day of our marriage to buy a *dog*?' the duchess queried.

'Not any old run-of-the-mill *dog*,' Mr. MacKenzie replied, slipping into his long johns. 'A *proper* wee black doggie.'

'I'm going with you,' the duchess replied. 'You must try to remember, Angus, that you are no longer a poor companionless bachelor, all alone in this world. I am, and will be, henceforth and forevermore, at your side.' And with that, Her Grace got out of her side of the bed. Thirty minutes later, after having braced themselves for the rigours of the journey with about four fingers of Royal Highland Dew Straight Scots Whisky, the dowager duchess and her consort rather regally descended the main staircase of Folkestone Castle, entered the ducal Rolls-Royce and set out for the Scottish Highlands.

They returned four days later with not one but two Scottish wolfhounds, of differing genders. The male wee black doggie, despite a rather awesome appearance, was frankly something of a disappointment to Mr. MacKenzie. Not only did it make it quite clear, almost from the beginning, that his heart belonged to the dowager duchess, but also that he lived in deep, unquestioned fear of the female wee black doggie. The latter (since two names were obviously required) was immediately dubbed Babykins, the dowager duchess having decided that Mr. MacKenzie's suggestion for a name (Wee Bitch), while technically correct, was somewhat

32

unsuitable for an animal which would, after all, be residing in the ducal apartments of Folkestone Castle.

Babykins turned out to be, as she grew, something of a mixed blessing. On one hand, she manifested most of the character traits of her breed which had endeared her predecessors to her master. That is to say, she grew both enormous and fearless, and was never happier than when she believed she was defending her master against the enemy. There were some problems with this (for one thing, she formed the idea that the in-grounds transport vehicle provided for the chief of staff was an infernal device intended to harm Mr. MacKenzie. She took great delight in biting the tyres, ripping the shredded rubber from the wheels, and carrying it proudly into the castle to drop at her master's feet), but nothing that, considering the breed, was really unexpected.

What really did annoy Mr. MacKenzie was that Babykins did not display, at all, what Mr. MacKenzie considered to be the appropriate dignified decorum of a wee black doggie. All of her male predecessors had been quite content to manifest their affection for their master with nothing more than a slow wag of the tail at his sight and by laying quietly at his feet. Not so Babykins. She deeply loved her master and didn't care if the whole world knew it.

When he left her, she howled in sorrow and frustration. When she saw him, she wagged her five-foot tail like a cocker spaniel, jumped up and down in unrestrained joy, and began to yelp with such enthusiasm and volume that more than one busload of jolly journeyers intending to spend the day (one pound sixpence, tax included) on the grounds of Folkestone Castle, upon hearing this sound, had made a sharp U-turn and sped off whence they had come.

The only way to shut Babykins up, Mr. MacKenzie quickly learned, was to wrestle her to the floor and scratch her belly. And the trouble with that was, of course, that Babykins could be wrestled to the floor only if she wished to be wrestled to the floor. She was just as likely not to wish to be wrestled to the floor, in which case she would knock Mr. MacKenzie to the floor, hold him in place with her right front paw, and demonstrate her unbounded affection for him by wetly licking his face and ears with her large, red, sand-papery tongue.

Babykins' puppy-like behaviour, the dowager duchess announced, would probably end with her maturity. The dowager duchess erred. The only thing that maturity did to Babykins was cause her to leap upon Wee Black Doggie with a new curious glint in her large yellow eyes. She no longer curled her lips back over her teeth at the sight of Wee Black Doggie, sending him racing away in fear for his life. At first it appeared to be mild curiosity, but towards the end of what the dowager duchess referred to with a coy smile as 'the courtship', Babykins became positively flirtatious.

For a while, truth to tell, Mr. MacKenzie had begun to suspect that this last Wee Black Doggie was going to disgrace his stalwart masculine predecessors even more, to the ultimate degree, in other words. But then came the day when Brigadier Fyffe appeared in the ducal apartments to announce, somewhat red-faced, that the reason for the enormous crowd in the formal gardens was that Babykins and Wee Black Doggie were, so to speak, in congress amidst the tulips. Two matrons from Baston-on-Thystle had fainted at the sight.

That business out of the way, Babykins thereafter chased Wee Black Doggie away whenever she saw him and settled down in the nursery of the castle to await the blessed day. She did, as befit an expectant mother, behave with somewhat more decorum during this period. She no longer knocked Mr. MacKenzie to the ground to lick his face, contenting herself with putting her paws on his shoulders to accomplish the same thing.

Towards the end she would allow no one but Mr. MacKenzie, not even the duchess, in the nursery and would permit the ministrations of the veterinarian only if Mr. MacKenzie stood beside her, scratching her ears and cooing to her comfortingly.

She delivered herself, in due time, of seven wee black doggies. Within a couple of days of the birth, she would permit the duchess into the nursery, to bill and coo over the babies, but not the veterinarian, and certainly not Wee Black Doggie. When Wee Black Doggie stuck an understandably curious nose into the nursery to see his offspring, she flung herself at the door (fortunately closing it against herself in the process) with such rage and fury that Wee Black Doggie fled howling, tail tucked between his legs, to the furthest corner of the Folkestone Castle Ltd. property.

All the pups (five males and two females) survived and prospered. Within a few weeks, they were bounding about the nursery with playful yelps, fighting each other for lunch, so to speak, when they were not gnawing Babykins' ears, nose, legs and other extremities. It was a touching sight, and the dowager duchess and Mr. MacKenzie, both of whom were childless, spent many happy hours in the nursery vicariously sharing Babykins' joy of parenthood.

Weaning time arrived. The subject of what to do with Babykins' babies had, of course, been discussed between the dowager duchess and Mr. MacKenzie at some length. Selling the pups was obviously out of the question; they were part of the family. Giving them away was the only answer, and long hours had been consumed discussing who was really entitled to the joy only a three-hundred-pound Scottish wolfhound could bring.

Three such fortunate souls were immediately identified. What better way to express the profound gratitude of the Folkestone family for the kindly medical care they gave to Woody Woodburn-Haverstraw (without even knowing that he was the duke) than to give them one of Babykins' babies? One of the females would go to the Reverend Mother Emeritus Margaret Houlihan Wachauf Wilson, R.N., of the God Is Love in All Forms Christian Church, Inc., of New Orleans, Louisiana. Male puppies would be sent to Dr. Benjamin Franklin Pierce and to Dr. John Francis Xavier McIntyre.

The second female pup would go to Esther Flanagan, R.N., also of the Spruce Harbor Medical Center. That left three male pups. One of these, obviously just had to go to Boris Alexandrovich Korsky-Rimsakov, the world's greatest opera singer. Not only was the present duke one of his greatest fans, but during an unfortunate misunderstanding at the time of the late duke's final rites, he had found himself in a fistfight with Mr. MacKenzie and had fought with such skill (the event was a draw) and enthusiasm that he and Mr. MacKenzie had naturally become rather close friends. Another darling little pup obviously had to go to Colonel Jean-Pierre de la Chevaux, president and chairman of the board of the Chevaux Petroleum Corporation, International, another of the young duke's new American friends who had also earned Mr. MacKenzie's profound, and seldom given, respect for efficacy and all-around skill in a streetbrawl situation.

That left one pup. But the solution to that problem could be deferred. There was always one runt of the litter, even with a splendid litter such as Babykins'. Long after his brothers and sisters had taken to taking their sustenance from bowls, one small male, who had come to be called 'Wee Black Runt', was still, so to speak, going home to mother for breakfast, lunch and dinner.

CHAPTER FOUR

That left only one problem, the solution for which was nowhere in sight. While Babykins seemed willing to accept (indeed, seemed relieved) that most of her family was now taking its meals elsewhere, her maternal instincts were strong.

Her pups could do what they willed, bound around the nursery, playfully tearing up pillows, solid oak furniture, joints of beef and each other, so long as they were not out of her sight for more than ten seconds at a time.

Mr. MacKenzie, from the very beginning, had been allowed to pick up the puppies, and when they were still comparatively tiny (no more than thirty pounds) she extended this privilege to the duchess and to the veterinarian. But when anyone else got even close to her offspring, back would go the lips over the glistening white teeth, up would go the thick bristles of hair from her neck to her tail, and out of her quivering throat would come her vocal expression of disapproval, a growl of a rather unearthly quality at a level of volume which caused the Austrian chandeliers throughout the castle to rattle alarmingly.

Weaning the puppies had posed no problem; the puppies had solved that themselves. Getting the puppies away from Babykins, so that they could be shipped to their new owners, was apparently going to be something of a problem.

Brigadier Fyffe, aware of this problem, was not at all surprised to learn from the upstairs butler that Her Grace and Mr. MacKenzie were in the nursery, trying again to separate Babykins, if only for a few minutes (to sort of get her used to the idea), from her babies.

Since the brigadier made many trips daily to the castle, and since there was sufficient cargo space (where golf clubs would normally have been carried) in the in-grounds transport vehicle, he had naturally fallen into the habit of delivering the puppies' rations himself. Babykins had come to tolerate him, and when she saw him come into the nursery, although she bared her teeth, she neither growled nor attempted to eat him.

'Good morning, Brigadier,' the dowager duchess greeted him. 'Isn't that sweet? Babykins' babies are glad to see you!'

Babykins' babies had, in fact, manifested their affection for the brigadier by knocking him to the ground and by playfully nibbling at his ears, nose, and other extremities, just as they did to their mother. The brigadier, not without effort, succeeded in freeing himself and climbed onto a stout oak banquet table.

'Your Grace,' he said, dabbing with his handkerchief at the blood leaking from a slight bite on his nose, 'Mr. MacKenzie. I fear I am the bearer of bad tidings.'

'And what might they be?' the dowager duchess inquired, somewhat coldly. 'Nothing, I trust, that will tend to cause red ink upon the ledger?'

'Worse, I fear, Your Grace,' Brigadier Fyffe replied.

'Out with it, man,' Mr. MacKenzie said. 'You old soldiers are forever beating about the bush.'

'Your Grace,' Brigadier Fyffe said, coming to attention atop the oak table, 'it is my painful duty to inform you that the black Bengal tigress, Princess, has gone to that great jungle in the sky.'

'I see,' the dowager duchess said, trying without much success to maintain a stiff upper lip. It quivered, in fact, and the duchess put a hand to her eye to wipe away a tear. 'Poor thing,' she said.

'And the cubs?' Mr. MacKenzie asked. He blew his nose rather loudly. He too had admired Princess.

'One was stillborn, Mr. MacKenzie,' Brigadier Fyffe said.

'And the other?'

'Alive, sir,' Fyffe replied. 'But the veterinary surgeon, I must tell you, offers little hope for his continued existence.'

'Oh, my!' the duchess said and started to sniffle. 'The poor little motherless thing!'

'Stop your bloody snivelling,' Mr. MacKenzie said rather curtly. 'Where there's life there's hope, as I always say.'

38

'Angus,' the dowager duchess said, 'you are always so profound!'

'That I am,' Mr. MacKenzie said. 'Well, Brigadier, let's go have a look at him.'

'Angus,' the duchess said, 'you'll have to go alone. I couldn't face a situation like that.'

'I understand, Dumplin',' Mr. MacKenzie said. 'Why don't you go fix yourself a little snort, and I'll take care of this tragic situation?'

'Oh, snookums, how did I ever get along without you? You're my own Rock of Gibraltar in time of pain and anguish!'

'Don't get carried away, old girl,' Mr. MacKenzie said. He turned and started out of the nursery. 'Come along, Fyffe.'

'Oh, Angus!' the dowager duchess cried when he had gone no more than fifty feet down the corridor.

'For God's sake, Florabelle, now what?' Mr. MacKenzie replied.

'Babykins is following you,' the dowager duchess replied. 'She doesn't want you to leave her.'

Babykins had indeed gotten to her feet and was walking after Mr. MacKenzie and Brigadier Fyffe.

'Florabelle,' Angus said, 'catch Wee Black Runt.' Wee Black Runt was tagging along after his mother.

'Do I dare?' the dowager duchess replied, somewhat nervously.

'We'll never know, will we, Florabelle, whether Babykins will bite you for picking up Wee Black Runt until you try, now will we?' MacKenzie replied patiently.

To Brigadier Fyffe's considerable surprise, Babykins, although she bared her teeth briefly and watched carefully, did not attempt to reclaim Wee Black Runt from the dowager duchess, even when the dowager duchess picked the pup up and growled rather convincingly back at him.

'Wee Black Runt,' MacKenzie said, 'I hate to tell you this, but it would appear that your rations-in-kind have just been shut off.'

Both the duchess and Brigadier Fyffe blushed, and the brigadier said, 'You really are a wag, .'

'I've always had a fine sense of humour, now that you mention it,' Mr. MacKenzie replied. 'Come along, brigadier.'

They descended the grand staircase and mounted the in-grounds transport vehicle.

'You're a *bad* girl!' Mr. MacKenzie said to Babykins as she opened her jaws to have at the tyre of the vehicle. '*Shame* on you!' Babykins closed her jaws, put her ears back and her tail between her legs and looked as if she was about to cry.

Fyffe put the vehicle in gear, and they rolled out of the courtyard and back through the castle grounds, with Babykins loping along behind them, until they reached the Cat House. Fyffe stopped the machine, and he and MacKenzie got off.

'Stay!' Mr. MacKenzie ordered. Babykins, a look of profound hurt on her face, obediently sat on her haunches. But the moment Mr. MacKenzie disappeared inside the Cat House, she raised her head and started to howl. The howl carried through the Cat House. The leopards and smaller felines, such as ocelots and wildcats, immediately disappeared inside their kennels. So did several magnificently maned lions. Only two lionesses apparently possessed the courage to face up to an animal who could make a sound like that. They started howling back.

MacKenzie came running back out, his kilt swinging from side to side.

'You're a *bad* girl, Babykins!' he said, shaking his finger in her face. Immediately, Babykins rose on her haunches, draped an enormous paw on each of MacKenzie's shoulders, and proceeded to kiss him, to show how sorry she was for being a bad girl and how appreciative she was for him not leaving her there all alone.

'Oh, come along with me,' he said. 'But try to behave. The last time you were in here, we had a hell of a time getting the lions calmed down.'

Babykins, tail wagging slowly from side to side, wearing what could only be described as a look of smug self-satisfaction on her face, followed her beloved master into the Cat House. Only when he passed the lionesses' cage did she deign to notice the animals in their cages. But when the larger of the two lionesses growled at her, she growled back. Both lionesses immediately rolled over on their backs, in the traditional gesture of subservience.

In the Cat House office, where a sort of incubator had been set up for the cub, she obediently sat where directed in the corner. The assistant cat keeper reported with regret that he couldn't get the cub to take any of the formula the veterinary surgeon had prescribed, even though (witness the pitiful little yelps) the cub was obviously hungry.

'Well, keep trying,' MacKenzie said. 'That's all you can do, keep trying.'

'I'm dreadfully sorry, Mr. MacKenzie,' the assistant cat keeper said.

'We're all sorry, lad,' Mr. MacKenzie replied. 'Brigadier, would you please take me back to the castle?'

Lost in thought, Mr. MacKenzie did not notice that Babykins did not immediately follow him. He had really opened his big mouth and put his foot in it. He had told Lambie-Pie that she shouldn't give up hope, and now there was no hope. There was no way in the world to keep a brand new tiger cub alive without its mother to feed it. He had no idea how he could phrase this gently for Lambie-Pie; he had really had little experience in his long life in phrasing things gently and delicately.

He got in the in-grounds transport vehicle, and Brigadier Fyffe drove him back slowly to the castle.

Neither of them, in other words, saw what Babykins did. Babykins' ears had perked up, and she had cocked her head to one side when she heard the pitiful little yelps from the incubator.

She rose from her haunches and made for the incubator.

'Get away from there, dog!' the assistant cat keeper had immediately protested, in what must be honestly described as the faintest of whispers. He also made threatening gestures of a sort: he moved the fingers of his left hand ever so slightly at her.

Babykins pushed her nose through the dark blanket covering the incubator. Her head disappeared inside. The pitiful yelping

41

stopped. Babykins withdrew her head from the incubator, growled *pro forma* at the assistant cat keeper, and then trotted back out of the Cat House, deigning to look neither right nor left at the caged lions, tigers and other felines.

When she was outside, she saw that the in-grounds transport vehicle had already departed; she could see it, the Union Jack proudly flying beside the brigadier's flag, turning the corner past the Ducal Roller Coaster, near the entrance to the Torture Dungeons Tour. She picked up speed, not running really, but rather loping with a certain grace.

Here and there in her path were guests of the castle, each of whom had paid his or her two shillings and whom she knew she was not allowed to eat. When they got in her way, she scattered them with a minor (3.2 on a scale of 1 to 10) growl and continued to close the gap between herself and her beloved master, riding disconsolately in the ex-golf cart.

When she had caught up with the vehicle, she slowed her pace and dutifully plodded along behind it until it got to the castle and her master got off. Then she followed him into the castle, down the great hall, and up the great stairway to the ducal apartments.

The dowager duchess was waiting at the head of the stairs.

'I've got something to tell you, Dumplin',' Mr. MacKenzie said to the duchess, deep regret in every syllable.

'Isn't that *darling*?' the duchess replied. 'Oh, Snookums, I knew you'd be able to do something.'

'I said for you to have one snort, not the whole bloody bottle,' he replied. 'What are you gushing over, anyway?'

The dowager duchess pointed down the stairway.

Babykins was coming up the wide steps with at least as much dignity as any member of the nobility. Her tread was sure; her tail swung with a measured dignity; her head was high and held firmly but with exquisite tenderness; and between her massive front teeth was a small, wet black object which gave out piteous mewing noises.

'Jesus H. Kee-rist!' the consort of Her Grace the Dowager Duchess of Folkestone said. 'Will you look at that?'

'Angus,' the duchess said, 'if you don't mind my saying so, language like that is most inappropriate at a time like this.'

Babykins marched past the dowager duchess and down the corridor to the nursery. She put a paw out and pushed the door open. Her puppies, seeing their mother, rushed to greet her. She gave off a growl from the very depths of her. The puppies skidded to a halt and then fled to a far corner of the nursery, where they huddled together for comfort. Most of them buried their heads under their brothers and sisters. Only Wee Black Runt had the courage (or perhaps the foolhardiness) to raise his head from the squirming pile as his mother resumed her position on an extraordinarily large red goatskin Moroccan hassock which had been brought from that country by the seventh duke (1801–1843) and only recently pressed into service.

Babykins lay down, arranged herself, and then turned and gently lowered the small, wet black bundle onto the hassock. With her nose, she directed the cub to a conveniently located source of nourishment in that area. A small black mouth opened, revealing a pale pink mouth. The mouth closed on a source of nourishment. The piteous mewing ceased. Babykins' long, large red tongue came out and began to bathe the cub.

Wee Black Runt, in both curiosity and outrage that someone else was moving in on the family restaurant (which only recently had been his alone), came bounding across the nursery floor. His mother growled a warning. He slowed his pace but kept coming. Babykins' lips drew back, and she continued to growl. Wee Black Runt sniffed at the newcomer. His mother watched him closely. The growling continued. Wee Black Runt's tongue came out and licked the newcomer.

'Snookums, look!' the dowager duchess said. 'Wee Black Runt thinks it's his baby brother!'

Whatever Wee Black Runt thought, it was obvious, even to his mother, that he meant the orphaned cub no harm. Babykins' growling ceased. Wee Black Runt joined his stepbrother for lunch.

Time passed. Against all odds, contrary to all the predictions of the veterinary profession, the cub (who was known, of course, as Wee Baby Brother) flourished in Babykins' care. Wee Black Runt displayed a rather touching

43

concern for the cub. When Wee Baby Brother first left Babykins' presence, Wee Black Runt was at his side. When his brothers and sisters displayed what Wee Black Runt apparently considered an unfriendly interest, Wee Black Runt defended him with such ferocity and tenacity that it not only warmed the cockles of Mr. MacKenzie's heart but made it unnecessary for Babykins to interfere.

Within a matter of just a month or two, of course, his fraternal protection was no longer necessary. Wee Baby Brother had learned that the way to deal with his new family was to arch his back, hiss at them in warning, and if that didn't work, to give them a good one across the chops with his right paw. That always worked, and soon peace, or really more an armed truce, reigned supreme.

Wee Black Runt, moreover, and as sometimes happens, suddenly began to grow. Soon he was the largest of the litter, and it became necessary for Babykins to protect the rest of the litter from Wee Black Runt, and Wee Baby Brother, rather than the reverse. Between the two of them, and they worked as a team, they frankly made the lives of their brothers and sisters miserable. They could handle Wee Black Runt's greater size, but there was no defence whatever against a ninety-pound black Bengal tiger cub who leapt to the attack from great heights, hissing, spitting, and flailing around with sharp claws at the end of each paw.

It was for this reason that the dowager duchess and Mr. MacKenzie finally bit the bullet, their discussion following a long (and frankly somewhat liquid) dinner in the dining room of the Sword, Crown & Anchor Hotel in London.

The dowager duchess of Folkestone and Mr. MacKenzie visited the Sword, Crown & Anchor as Sergeant Major (Retired) MacKenzie and Missus. The habitués of that establishment, retired or active Royal Marines (plus a handful of U.S. Marines assigned to the U.S. embassy and given honorary membership), had found it hard enough to believe that Black Dog MacKenzie had married at all. It would have been beyond belief that he had married the senior member of one of England's noblest families and was now listed in the current Burke's *Peerage*.

44

On the night in question, Angus MacKenzie, shyly acknowledging a lengthy round of applause for his performance (a medley of 'Braes of Melinigh,' 'The Flowers of the Forest Land O' the Leal,' and 'Mrs. MacPherson of Inveran', set his bagpipes down and marched none too steadily back to his table and his bride.

He helped himself to four fingers of Royal Highland Dew Straight Scots Whisky, tossed it down, and poured another four fingers into his glass.

'Florabelle, darlin' . . .' he began.

'What is it, Snookums?' Florabelle replied.

'Dumplin',' he said, 'we have got to kick the babies out of the nest.'

Florabelle began to sniffle.

'That won't help a bit,' Angus said. 'I feel as bad about it as you, Dumplin'.'

'But they're but eight months old,' she said. 'Still wee babies.'

'I weighed the little one,' Angus said. 'Eleven stone, Dumpling, that's what she weighed. God knows what Wee Black Runt weighs.'

'Not Wee Black Runt! Not our Wee Black Runt! I couldn't bear to turn Wee Black Runt loose, all alone in a cruel world!'

'We'll be keeping Wee Black Runt and Wee Baby Brother, Dumpling,' Mr. MacKenzie said. 'I've already tol' ye that. But the others have to go. It's the only decent thing to do. They deserve people of their own.'

'You're right, of course, Angus,' the dowager duchess said with a stiff upper lip. 'You're always right.'

'I keep telling you that.'

'I shudder at the thought, however, of our babies huddled frightened and alone in shipping crates, not knowing where they're going, not knowing why they have been suddenly torn from home and hearth.'

'I'm two steps ahead of ye, Dumplin',' Angus replied. 'The Wog's going to take care of everything.'

'I do wish you would not refer to His Royal Highness by that appellation,' the dowager duchess said.

'He calls me "Scotty" and I call him "Wog",' MacKenzie replied. 'What's wrong with that?'

'Angus, far be it from me to criticize you for anything, but really, one should not refer to His Royal Highness Crown Prince Hassan ad Kayam, Heir Apparent to the Kingdom of Hussid, Ambassador Extraordinary and Plenipotentiary to the Fourth French Republic, the Court of Saint James's and the United States of America, as "The Wog".'

'Well, that's what he is, isn't he? And besides, that's why I asked him for help.'

'I don't quite understand you, Snookums,' the dowager duchess said.

'For a wog, he's really a decent sort,' Angus said. 'When I spoke with him on the phone about sending Boris one of the puppies, he brought it up himself.'

'What did he bring up himself?'

'He said the very least he could do, since we were giving one of the puppies to Boris, was to send that ugly plane for him.'

'You mean, he's going to send a La Discorde* to England to pick up Boris' puppy?'

'Not only that, Dumplin',' Angus said, 'he's going to deliver the others in it, too.'

'That certainly is very gracious of His Royal Highness,' Dumpling replied.

'Him being a diplomat and all, he said,' Angus went on, 'that way we get around all the red tape about shipping dogs across international borders. "No Doggie, No Oily," was the way the Wog put it. He's got a certain way with words.'

---

*La Discorde of course, is the droop-nosed French supersonic jetliner. Unquestionably the world's fastest passenger aircraft, it is also the most expensive to operate. Of the five which have been built, three were purchased by the Royal Hussid government, HRH Prince Hassan having been deeply affected by the piteous entreaties of the French minister of aviation, who said that unless Hussid bought some, none would be sold. Only Hussid, with a population of less than a million, but with oil reserves second only to Saudi Arabia (they provide 38 per cent of France's petroleum), could afford to fly the aircraft.

CHAPTER FIVE

Three days later, a rather interesting convoy of vehicles rolled down Paris' Boulevard Saint Michel. Preceded by a Land-Rover carrying a half-dozen robed Arab-types, each armed with a chrome-plated submachine gun, the roof a veritable forest of flashing lights, screaming sirens and whooping whoopers, next came two Citroën sedans, black in colour and each bearing CORPS DIPLOMATIQUE insignia on front and rear bumpers. Next in line was a Cadillac limousine, from whose gleaming fenders flew an ornate, silk-embroidered flag. Two curved swords were shown crossed over the silhouette of an oil-drilling rig, and above this was the familiar dollar sign. It was, of course, the somewhat less than beloved national emblem of the kingdom of Hussid. Behind the Cadillac came another Citroën sedan, and, bringing up the rear, still another Land-Rover.

At every major intersection the gendarmes on duty snapped to attention and threw the convoy a splendid salute. The word had come down, in no uncertain terms, from the Quai d'Orsay that there were two very good reasons why it behoved every patriotic Frenchman to extend every possible courtesy, professional and otherwise, to the diplomatic representative (and heir apparent) of His Most Islamic Majesty Sheikh Moulay Hassan of Hussid. The first, of course, was that France drew 38 per cent of its petroleum needs from beneath Hussid's arid sands and did not wish to do anything at all that might endanger the source of the supply.

The second, equally important reason was the ambassador himself. His Royal Highness Crown Prince Hassan ad Kayam had been, as everyone knew, the only customer for La Discorde aircraft, and that certainly should earn him a warm place in the hearts of every Frenchman. Most other senior foreign officials had shaken their heads sadly when offered an opportunity to purchase a La Discorde, and a few of the ill-bred had actually laughed out loud at the suggestion.

47

The back seat of the Cadillac today held a full complement of passengers, including two on the jump seats. This was out of the ordinary, because HRH seldom chose to ride with members of his staff. Today, however, three of the four normal occupants of the Citroën which customarily rode immediately before the Cadillac in the procession were riding with His Royal Highness.

This change in protocol had been made necessary by the necessity of transporting a dog from Orly Field to the Paris Opera House. The pup, (he was, after all, only eight months old) had demonstrated an immediate and violent dislike for HRH's staff. It had only been with some effort that he had been kept from eating them and forced into the Citroën's back seat by one of HRH's staff, using a chair and the techniques of a lion tamer.

As the Citroën turned off the Boulevard Saint Michel onto the Rue de Rivoli, His Royal Highness, riding in the Cadillac behind, could see that the animal was cheerfully tearing up the upholstery in the back seat of the Citroën and pawing playfully at the glass which separated the back seat from the front seat.

From the Rue de Rivoli the convoy turned onto L'Avenue de l'Opéra, raced down that street through the Place de l'Opéra, and made a sweeping U-turn to pull up beside the stage door of the French National Opera House. The moment the cars stopped, the chauffeur of the Citroën leapt out of the driver's seat and fled screaming towards the safety of the Café de la Paix, located just across the street.

'Highness,' one of HRH's staff inquired, 'what do we do now?'

'Form a skirmish line around the car,' HRH ordered. 'See that the animal does not escape.'

'We may, of course, shoot the beast to preserve life and limb?' the staff member inquired, rather too hopefully.

'Of course not,' HRH replied. 'You idiot, that dog is the property of the Maestro!'

'Forgive me, Your Highness,' the man said and got out of the car and gave the necessary instructions. Finally, His

Highness himself got out of the limousine. He was a true son of the desert, with the flashing eyes, finely trimmed beard and moustache one expects to see on a son of the desert. He would, however, have made a somewhat more imposing picture had it not been for his height and weight. His Highness stood five-feet-four and weighed one-hundred-ninety pounds, not counting the four pounds of golden rope with which his head-dress was affixed to his round little head.

His Highness sort of waddled up the stairway to the main door of the opera. A gendarme pulled the door open for him and bowed.

The moment the door was open, His Highness smiled. He could hear the Maestro, Boris Alexandrovich Korsky-Rimsakov, the world's greatest opera singer, and, for the past four years, an official national treasure of the French Republic, singing.

The Maestro was in good form, His Highness noted. The chandeliers were rattling.

A gendarme stood before each door to the auditorium. Boris Alexandrovich Korsky-Rimsakov refused to have a bunch of freeloaders gaping while he was rehearsing; visitors were forbidden. There were exceptions, of course, and His Highness was one of the two. (The other was the president of the Republic.) His Highness was bowed through by another gendarme. He stayed in the back of the auditorium until the Maestro had concluded his aria (Leicester's aria from Act III of Donizetti's *Maria Stuarda*, 'Oh, savage woman, a sister's death warrant you have signed ...' etc.) and then he applauded and shouted, 'Bravo! Bravo!'

Maestro Boris Alexandrovich Korsky-Rimsakov, who had been, in his role, looking shocked, aghast and heart-sick, his hand held dramatically across his face, now stood up. He faced the audience, which he could not see, of course, because of the lights.

'Who *dares* to intrude on *my* rehearsal?' he bellowed.

'It is I, Maestro, Hassan!' His Royal Highness called.

'Have you the puppy?'

'In a manner of speaking, Maestro,' His Highness replied.

'You either have it or you don't,' the singer replied. 'Is that so complicated?'

'It's in the car, Maestro,' Hassan replied.

'In the car? In the *car*? You disgust me, Hassan! Talk about cold, and cruel, only a backward Arab who takes his perverted pleasure from torturing a helpless animal would leave a helpless puppy in a car on a day like this.' He started off the stage.

'Maestro,' the conductor asked, 'what about the rehearsal?'

'Don't be such a callous ass,' the Maestro said. 'How could you possibly expect me to sing, now that I've gotten, firsthand, another sickening example of man's inhumanity to beast?'

Coming up the aisle, dressed in the costume of the earl of Leicester, the singer made quite an appearance. He stood six feet six inches tall and weighed just over two-hundred-eighty pounds. The luxuriant beard which covered his chin and cheeks was all his. His dark eyes flashed.

'Maestro,' His Royal Highness said, 'it's a gorgeous spring day out there. The temperature is exactly seventy-two degrees Fahrenheit. And the car is air-conditioned. The pup is perfectly comfortable!'

'All alone,' the singer said. 'At a tender period in his puppyhood, when he needs loving companionship above all else!' He strode purposefully past His Royal Highness, burst out into the foyer and descended to the street. He had no trouble locating the car. It was ringed with a line of Arabs in robes.

Boris strode up to the Citroën. the pup, slavering somewhat from its mouth and displaying a rather impressive set of choppers, was pawing at the window. It was clear to everyone but Boris that he wanted nothing more than to eat an Arab.

'Look!' Boris said. 'He's glad to see me! He knows that he's mine!'

'Maestro,' Hassan said somewhat breathlessly, for he'd had to run to keep up with the singer, 'if I were you, I wouldn't open that door!'

Boris opened the door and then turned.

'What did you say?'

At that point, the pup reached out and nipped Boris on the hand. Boris yelped. The dog, growling mightily, retreated about two inches and seemed prepared to leap again.

Boris looked at his hand. A couple of drops of blood, no larger than pencil points, showed where the skin had been just barely lacerated. Boris looked at it with mixed rage and horror.

'That flea-ridden Hound of the Baskervilles has *bitten* Boris Alexandrovich Korsky-Rimsakov!' he announced. 'Bitten *me*! His *master*!'

'I'll have him shot immediately,' Hassan said, snapping his fingers. With obvious pleasure, two bodyguards rushed up and worked the actions of their submachine guns.

Boris sent both of them flying, one with each massive arm. Then he bent over to lean in the car.

'Come out of there, you furry Benedict Arnold!' he said angrily, when he emerged he had the dog (which weighed, at about half of its ultimate size, only about one-hundred-fifty pounds) by the scruff of the neck.

The animal snarled, twisted, and snapped.

'*Bad* doggie!' Boris Alexandrovich Korsky-Rimsakov said at full volume. 'It's not nice to bite your daddy!' The pup had not (and as far as that goes, few people have) heard an admonition administered that close to the ear and at that volume by Boris Alexandrovich Korsky-Rimsakov. In something close to abject terror, it stopped snarling, twisting, and snapping. Boris then grabbed the forepaw, put it between his teeth, and closed his jaws. 'Get the idea?' he said. The pup yelped. 'Now, we'll have no more of that, will we?'

He set the dog down in the street. The dog looked up at him, ears back, hunched over.

'Well, you asked for it, you stupid beast!' Boris said, but the tone was somewhat softer, and the dog sensed it. The tail made a timid, tentative wag; the head cocked.

'You may not be too bright,' Boris said to him, 'but you're sure a good-looking hound.'

The tail wagged with more confidence now, sweeping back and forth on the cobblestones. The ears rose. The dog seemed to smile.

'If you'll promise to be a good boy,' Boris cooed, 'Daddy will forgive you!'

The dog rose on his haunches and laid his paws on Boris' massive chest. He made whimpering noises of joy and love. His tongue came out and lapped at Boris' beard. He had found a master he could love and respect.

'You hungry, Prince?' Boris asked.

'I thought we might drop by Le Tour de l'Argent,' His Royal Highness replied, making reference to one of Paris' best restaurants, the name of which aptly translates as 'the tower of money.'

'I'm speaking to the dog, you idiot,' Boris said. 'I suppose it's too much to expect that you have thought about providing this helpless puppy with something to eat?'

'The duchess, Maestro, sent a recommended formula for its feeding. One of my men is acquiring the ingredients and will take them to your apartment.'

'And in the meantime, this motherless waif is supposed to go hungry?' Boris said. 'You are really a cold and callous person, Hassan. I don't know why I put up with you.'

With that, he pushed the dog's paws off his chest and walked to the Cadillac. The dog, without being told, followed him. Hassan followed the dog. Boris sat on the far side of the seat. The dog got up and sat in the middle of the seat. Somewhat nervously, Hassan got in beside them. The dog turned to look at Hassan. His tongue came out and licked His Royal Highness' ear.

'See there?' Boris said. 'Prince likes you. God knows why!' He leaned forward on the seat to speak to the chauffeur. 'Take us to Maxim's,' he ordered. 'Phone ahead and tell them to lay out a large buffet of their best edible garbage ... meat only, no crepes suzette or anything unhealthy like that ... for my puppy dog.'

'Yes, Maestro,' the chauffeur replied.

The singer sat back on the velour upholstery of the seats. The dog nuzzled him.

'God, I hope you're housebroken,' Boris said.

'Maestro,' His Royal Highness said, 'might I presume to ask two questions?'

'That would, of course, depend on the questions,' Boris replied. 'You'll have to take your chances.'

'You address the animal as "Prince",' His Royal Highness said. 'Might I have the temerity to inquire why?'

'When I was just a wee tyke,' Boris replied, his eyes watering at the memory, 'in Hoboken, New Jersey, my only true pal was my dog. His name was "Prince", and when the other guys laughed at me for singing all the time, Prince would make them stop.'

'I see,' His Highness said, sympathetically.

Prince licked Boris' ear. His Royal Highness withdrew a silk handkerchief from his robes and blew his nose rather loudly.

'Oh, how I missed that dog!' Boris said, his chest heaving. 'After he was gone, that bully Curly Chris made my life miserable!'

As Boris' friend of long standing, His Highness knew that it was time to change the subject.

'Dear Maestro,' he said as the limousine rolled majestically across the Place de la Concorde and up the Avenue des Champs Elysées, 'you mentioned before that you had had splendid news?'

'So I did,' the singer said. He sat up. 'I don't suppose you've got another handkerchief, do you? Prince, in demonstrating his boundless affection for me, has slobbered all over my neck.'

A fresh handkerchief was produced from within the crown prince's billowing robes, and the singer mopped at his neck and ear.

'You were mentioning the splendid news you had received?' Hassan pursued.

'So I was,' Boris said. 'The sainted guru of Manhattan, Kansas, is coming to Vienna!' His delight in this happening was evident in his voice.

'You don't say?' the crown prince replied. The singer was referring to Theosophilus Mullins Yancey, M.D., Ph.D.,

D.D., D.V.M., founder and director of the Joyful Practice Institute and Foundation of Manhattan, Kansas. After long and painstaking research, Dr. Yancey had concluded that one form of exercise was clearly superior to jogging, deep knee bends, weight lifting, deep breathing, swimming, horseback riding . . . indeed, all other exercise. After publishing his findings,* he soon found himself rather lionized by those who realized he had uncovered a deep and profound truth. One of his first disciples was Boris Alexandrovich Korsky-Rimsakov, who had, he said, been thinking along those lines himself, although he of course had not the background or education to do anything but conduct the most rudimentary experiments.

Upon reading the first volume, the singer had written to Dr. Yancey offering the most flattering appraisal of the work and volunteering, for the doctor's files, some of his own experiences with healthful exercise. Some of these (for example, 'Some Aspects of Exercise Within a Pressurized Aircraft Cabin at Altitudes Over 30,000 Feet') were published (pseudonymously of course) in the foundation's monthly journal *Joyful Practice* and others (for example, 'Too Much Is Bad for You? Nonsense!') as separate, paperbound monographs, at $1.95.

The singer, absolutely convinced that his dedicated adherence to Dr. Yancey's theories had been of unquestioned value to his singing career, to the superb timbre and range of his voice itself, had graciously endorsed his royalty checks over to the Joyful Practice Institute. He had moreover, recommended Dr. Yancey without reservation for membership in the Matthew Q. Framingham Theosophical Foundation, of Cambridge, Massachusetts, into which body the philosopher-physician had been readily accepted.

They had not, however, (although they had spoken at length on the telephone), ever had the opportunity to meet face-to-face.

---

*See *Sexual Intercourse as Exercise*, 245 pp. (illustrated), $8.95, and *Strength and Health Through Constant Coitus*, 235 pp., $7.95, both by Theosophilus Mullins Yancey, M.D., Joyful Practice Publishing Company, Manhattan, Kansas.

'Indeed, I do say,' Boris replied. 'The beloved physician will, of course, be my guest.'

'In Vienna?'

'I *said* he was going to Vienna. Some sort of shrinks' convention, I gather.'

'But you took a solemn vow never to go to Vienna again as long as you lived.'

'I did no such thing!'

'Maestro, forgive me, but I seem to remember you saying those exact words just before you removed your bust from the lobby and carried it out of the opera house.'

'I don't recall it at all,' Boris said. 'Are you sure?'

'The *Wiener Kourier*'s opera critic had suggested that you weren't quite up to form, as I recall.'

'It's a little vague in my memory.'

'You don't recall throwing your bust at the music critic, either? Through the plate-glass window at Demels?'

'I wondered what had happened to it,' Boris replied blandly. 'Well, no matter. I have chosen to forgive them. Find out when the Albert Schweitzer of the Plains will be in Vienna, then get in touch with the opera house and tell them I will sing, no more than twice, during that period. And make sure they have my suite in Sacher's Hotel redecorated. We want nothing but the best for the doctor, right?'

'I'll do what I can, of course,' His Royal Highness said.

'That's what you're for, Hassan, after all, isn't it?' Boris said.

'As soon as I return from the United States.'

'Why are you going to the States?'

'I volunteered to deliver the other puppies for the duchess,' Hassan replied.

'What *other* puppies? I was given to believe I was the *only* one getting one of these splendid beasts and all-around friends of man.'

'There are five others on the plane now, Maestro,' Hassan said. 'I thought you knew.'

'How could I possibly know? With you and the duchess in a nefarious conspiracy to keep me from finding out? Who gets the others?'

55

'Dr. Hawkeye and Dr. Trapper John get one each, as does Nurse Flanagan.'

Nurse Flanagan did not rank high in Boris' esteem. She had once laughed at him in a time of great pain and anguish. (On a fishing trip Prince Hassan had hooked Boris in what was medically described as the epidermal covering of the gluteus maximus. Nurse Flanagan had found what she called 'fish-hooks in the can' amusing; she had actually laughed.)

'That Irish harridan gets one? And Hot Lips does not?'

'Hot Lips, too, of course, Maestro. Each of the ladies gets a bitch.'

'You said five others?'

'And Horsey de la Chevaux the last,' Prince Hassan said. 'The duchess has kept the runt of the litter, as she put it.'

'Mine, of course, must be the pick of the litter,' Boris said. 'Angus MacKenzie would have seen to that.'

'I believe the selections were made by the dowager duchess herself, Maestro. At least her handwriting was on the tags.'

'And what did Prince's tag say?'

'This is the meanest of the lot.'

'She obviously meant to say finest,' Boris replied. 'Well, here we are at Maxim's.'

'So we are.'

'You will, of course, leave the limousine for me and go to Orly Field in one of those ugly Frog cars,' Boris said as the chauffeur opened the door.

'I had hoped that we might have supper before I left for the States,' His Highness replied.

'Don't be absurd! How could you possibly sit in here and stuff your face, knowing that all the time five motherless puppies are sitting all alone on the La Discorde? Get going!'

'You're right, of course,' His Royal Highness said.

'Hassan,' Boris said as an afterthought, 'be sure to invite everyone to hear me sing in Vienna. They won't come, of course, but simply being invited brings a ray of sunshine into their dreary little lives.'

'Of course, Maestro, as you wish,' His Highnsess said.

Hassan changed cars. Boris Alexandrovich Korsky-Rimsakov and Prince marched into Maxim's. They marched past the riffraff in the tables on the sidewalk, and in the inside restaurant, Boris acknowledging the applause, ooohs, aaahs and hotel-room keys which his feminine fans threw in his direction with a gracious wave of his hand. The maître d'hôtel bowed them to a table in the section reserved for royalty, and the sommelier rushed up with a freshly chilled magnum of Piper Heidsieck '50.

The proprietor himself appeared.

'Maestro!' he called, clapping his hands together before him in ecstasy. 'How good of you to favour my humble establishment.'

'It was an emergency,' Boris replied. 'Stop standing there looking as if you are about to wet your pants and bring on the garbage.'

CHAPTER SIX

Lieutenant (Junior Grade) J. P. Jones, United States Navy, having been summoned to appear before Rear Admiral (Lower Half) J. Kingswood Saltee, U.S.N., at 1615 hours Zulu Time (11:15 A.M. Maryland time), had dressed in the proper uniform with extra care.

The navy had officially decreed the arrival of spring, and although there was a freezing drizzle outside, the summer white uniform was prescribed. The white uniform of Lieutenant (j.g.) Jones was crisp and spotless, from hat cover to shoes. The gold on the epaulets glistened. The knot in the tie was absolute perfection.

At 1616 Zulu, the admiral's yeoman spoke.

'The admiral will see you now, Lieutenant.'

'Thank you, yeoman,' Lieutenant (j.g.) J. P. Jones replied in a crisp naval manner, and marched into the admiral's office. Lieutenant Jones stopped the prescribed five feet from the admiral's desk and came to attention.

'Lieutenant (j.g.) Jones, J. P., reporting to the admiral as ordered sir,' Lieutenant (j.g.) Jones said.

'So I see, my dear,' the admiral replied, getting to his feet and fixing a broad smile on his ruddy, nautical face. 'And, if I may say so, my dear, you are a sight to really brighten the day of any sailor.'

Lieutenant (j.g.) Joanne Pauline Jones, U.S.N., said nothing. After all, lieutenants, even lady lieutenants, are not permitted to shout rude things at rear admirals (Lower Half).

'Please sit down, my dear young woman,' the admiral said, 'and make yourself comfortable. Is there anything I can get you? Cigarette? Coffee? How about a little martineroony?'

'No, thank you, sir.' Lieutenant Jones said. 'I make it a practice, sir, never to hoist the mainbrace, sir, either on duty, sir, or before the sun has passed over the yardarm sir.'

'Commendable attitude, Lieutenant,' the admiral said, visibly disappointed. 'But as your naval career progresses, you will come to understand that there are those occasions upon which it is entirely appropriate to bend navy regulations.'

'Yes, sir,' Lieutenant (j.g.) Jones replied, without much enthusiasm. She had joined the navy to see the world; to tread the bridge of a man-of-war; to feel the sea spray against her face; to chart new courses for women through previously male chauvinist pig seas. So far, all she had done was man a typewriter. And worse, been a uniformed baby-sitter.

Admiral Saltee turned from his bar and handed her a martini.

'Anchors aweigh, Lieutenant!' he said, extending a martini.

'I beg your pardon, sir.' Lieutenant (j.g.) Jones said, not taking the martini.

'Make all preparations to get under way!' the admiral went on. 'Cast off, fore and aft! All ahead full!'

'I'm afraid I don't follow you,' Lieutenant (j.g.) Jones said.

'The sailor's lingo will, I'm sure, my dear, come to you in time. In ladies' language then, what I'm telling you is that you're going to sea!'

'I'm going to sea?' Lieutenant (j.g.) Jones asked, unable to believe what she was hearing.

'You're going to sea,' the admiral confirmed. Lieutenant (j.g.) Jones practically snatched the martini glass out of his hand. She tossed it down.

'Yes, *sir*.' she said.

'And not, I hasten to add, on some hospital ship or some supply ship or some transport.'

'On a man-of-war, sir?' Lieutenant (j.g.) Jones asked, afraid to trust her great good fortune.

'Better than a man-of-war,' the admiral said, leaving her dangle in suspense while he refilled her glass and only then adding, 'on a nuclear sub!'

'On a nuclear sub,' Lieutenant (j.g.) Jones repeated, almost reverently.

'Anchors aweigh, Lieutenant!' the admiral replied.

'Thank you, sir,' Lieutenant Jones replied, blushing prettily and then raising her glass again.

'I have every confidence, my dear,' the admiral said, 'that you will discharge your extraordinary duties in a manner which will bring credit upon those other females whose names at the moment escape me, but who, I'm told, have, from time to time, been called upon to lend their peculiar female talents to the support of the navy's mission.'

Lieutenant (j.g.) Jones somehow didn't like the sound of that. It didn't sound as if her duties aboard the nuclear submarine were going to be much different from what they were here at the U.S. Naval Academy. A 'peculiar female talent' would not be necessary, she realized, if she were going to be assigned, for example, as navigator, or even mess officer.

'Sir,' she asked, gathering her courage, 'might I inquire as to the exact nature of my duties aboard the submarine?'

'For the moment, my dear, suffice it to say that you will be making a contribution of great value to the efficacy of the Nuclear Submarine Force, North Atlantic.'

'Yes, sir,' she said. 'And what does that mean, Admiral?'

'A contribution of more than mere naval importance,' he said, 'a contribution with grave diplomatic-political implications which normally . . . forgive my bluntness . . . would not be entrusted to a naval officer, particularly a lady naval officer, of such junior rank and short service.'

'I don't quite follow you, Admiral,' she said.

'In good time, my dear,' the admiral said. He punched the TRANSMIT button on his intercom. 'Yeoman, is the chopper standing by?'

'Yes, sir,' a somewhat metallic voice replied.

'I'll bet,' the admiral said, 'when you woke this morning, when you looked in the mirror at your pretty little face, it would never have occurred to you that you would be lunching with the secretary of state?'

'No, sir,' she said, somewhat confused, 'it would not have. It did not.'

'Come with me, my dear,' the admiral said. He took her arm and led her out of his office and out of the building. A Sikorsky helicopter, the type normally employed to circle an aircraft carrier during aircraft launch and recovery operations, to pluck those pilots who had made piloting errors from the briny deep, sat on the lawn, its pilot and crew chief leaning against the fuselage.

The engine started, and even as the admiral and Lieutenant (j.g.) Jones strapped themselves into rather elegant, plushly upholstered armchairs (the helicopter was normally assigned to the commandant of the naval academy, and he, of course, could not be expected to sit on aluminium pipe and nylon cloth seats like some common swabby), the rotor began to turn. It began to make a fluckta-fluckta noise and then suddenly leapt into the air.

The helicopter was equipped with a public address system, and the voice of the pilot came over it.

'Annapolis, Chopper Two-One off the ground at 1650 Zulu. VIP direct flight to the Department of State.'

'Roger, Annapolis Departure Control clears VIP Chopper Two-One to the roof to the State Department.'

Now this, thought Lieutenant (j.g.) Joanne Pauline Jones, was more like it. This is what she had in mind, flying in a navy helicopter, when she had left behind her a tearful mother, an apoplectic father and a somewhat cynical sixteen-year-old brother to don navy blue. And this was only the beginning. The admiral had said she was going to sea on a nuclear submarine, and admirals never lie.

In a very short time, the helicopter made a steep banking motion in the air. 'State Department, Navy VIP Two-One for landing on the roof,' the loudspeaker announced.

'Navy VIP Two-One is cleared to land on the roof,' a voice replied. The helicopter stopped forward movement, hovered in the air for a moment, and then fluttered, leaflike, to a helipad on the roof of the State Department Building.

The crew chief slid the door open, jumped out, put the pipe to his lips and blew mightily.

'Juniors first, my dear,' the admiral said, bowing Lieutenant (j.g.) Jones off the aircraft. She jumped to the roof. A short, rather plump, curly-haired gentleman was standing there, his fingers in his ears.

'Enough with the tweet-tweet already,' he said rather impatiently.

'Belay the piping,' the admiral said, then, 'Mr. Secretary,' he went on, saluting crisply, 'it was unnecessary for you to personally meet us.'

'I know dat,' the secretary said, 'but a liddle breath fresh air's good for you. My momma told me dat.'

'Mr. Secretary,' the admiral said, 'may I present Lieutenant Junior Grade Joanne Pauline Jones, U.S.N.?'

'A couple of years ago, dolling,' the secretary said somewhat poignantly, examining the naval officer's physique approvingly, 'but now I'm a happily married man.'

'How do you do, sir?' Lieutenant (j.g.) Jones said very formally.

'Very nice, tank you,' the secretary replied. 'The hair gets a liddle mussed from that whatchamacallit,' he indicated the rotor blade, 'but dat's vat dey sell combs for, right? You're hungry, I hope? I had the chef fix something special. Ve'll vork vhile ve eat, O.K.?'

He took Lieutenant (j.g.) Jones's arm and led her into the building, onto an elevator, and down long, highly polished corridors to a door marked SECRETARY'S DINING ROOM.

'Dat means me,' he explained helpfully. 'Nod duh gurls with duh shorthand.' He ushered them inside.

'So start vid duh movie already,' the secretary called after entering the room.

The lights dimmed, and a motion-picture screen descended from the ceiling.

The words 'ABSOLUTELY TOP SECRET' flashed on the screen. 'BY ORDER OF THE SECRETARY OF DEFENCE.'

Lieutenant (j.g.) Jones's heart beat a little faster. She was about to become privy to TOP SECRET material. That was something else that hadn't happened before in her naval career, even though she had been subjected to what is known as a Complete Background Investigation (or CBI)* by the Office of Naval Intelligence.

* A flock of sailors in civilian clothes, in other words, had circulated through her hometown and through her circle of university acquaintances, soliciting nasty thoughts and suspicions. When these had all been gathered together and prepared in seven copies, seven senior naval officers had sat

'NUCLEAR SUBMARINE FORCE, NORTH ATLANTIC' flashed on the screen, followed by 'U.S. NAVY BASE, HERSTEAD-ON-HEATH, ENGLAND.'

It was really a fascinating, well-put-together movie, taking the viewer not only into the interior of the nuclear submarines which prowled through the ocean's depths on months-long patrols but also into their supply and maintenance base at Herstead-on-Heath, England. It made it quite clear that, for a number of reasons, the base at Herstead-on-Heath was absolutely indispensable to the Nuclear Submarine Force, North Atlantic, and without stretching anything, to the entire defence posture of the United States of America.

And, she thought as the lights came on, her heart beating patriotically beneath her white tunic, *she* was going to be a part of all that!

'So, you don't mind telling me, vat do you tink about all dat?' the secretary said.

'It's inspiring, Mr. Secretary,' she said.

'Dat's vun vay to put it,' the secretary said. 'Duh vord I vas looking for, frankly, vas "indispensable". You vould agree, dolling, dat wit'out Herstead-on-Heath, we vould be, you should excuse duh expression, up duh creek wit'out a paddle?'

'Yes, sir, Mr. Secretary, I would say that.'

'You're a good girl. Your momma and poppa must be proud of you,' the secretary said.

Lieutenant (j.g.) Jones blushed again.

'Now here's vere you come in,' the secretary said. 'A liddle more background. Ve rent Herstead-on-Heath, pay a nice liddle price for it. Instead of own it. You get my meaning?'

'Yes, sir.'

'Duh fellow vot owns it is His Grace duh Duke of Folkestone. An Englisher.'

---

down at a table to officially conclude that Lieutenant (j.g.) Jones was not really a Soviet spy and could be trusted with the nation's deepest secrets, despite such damaging information in the dossier that she had seldom made her bed at college and had a 'perfectly disgusting' habit of drying her unmentionable with a hairblower.

'I see.'

'No, you don't, unless the admiral here's been running off at the mouth again,' the secretary said. He looked at the admiral. 'Hey, Admiral. Vake up! You been running around shooting off your mouth again?'

'The admiral has told me nothing,' Lieutenant (j.g.) Jones said.

'Not a word, sir!' the admiral said.

'Try to keep avake,' the secretary said. 'So, dolling, the admiral's been telling me vat a wonderful job you been doing as . . . vat's her job title, admiral?'

'Officer-in-Charge, Morale and Entertainment, Counselling and Advice, Non-American Midshipmen,' the admiral replied promptly.

'Vat he said, taking care of the foreigners at the academy,' the secretary said.

'May I ask what that has to do with this, Mr. Secretary?'

'Keep your pants on . . . you should excuse the expression, I'm getting to dat.'

'Yes, sir.'

'And among dese foreign midshipmen, I understand you get along special good vit one.'

'You mean Midshipman Woodburn-Haverstraw, sir?'

'Dat's duh vun,' the secretary said. 'You vant to tell me maybe a liddle aboud him?'

'Well, I don't really know what to say, sir. Woodburn-Haverstraw is a nice kid. He's an orphan, you see, and perhaps for that reason he understands what it's like to be alone. He's always doing something nice for the other foreign boys. He plays the piano for them, talks to them, that sort of thing.'

'And he likes you special, right?'

'There is nothing *romantic* in our relationship, Mr. Secretary, if that's what you are implying. Woody has a girl. A sweet girl. A student nurse. But we are good friends.'

'You know the girl, too, right? Ven you get right down to it, Lieutenant, on more den vun occasion, you haf sneaked Woodburn-Haverstraw off duh campus in the trunk of your Volkswagen so he could see duh girl, right?'

'I wasn't,' Lieutenant (j.g.) Jones said, after a long pause, 'aware that this was common knowledge.'

'Common knowledge it isn't. But dah bottom line, dolling, is dat you and dis boy are good friends, right?'

'His relationship with that girl is rather touching, Mr. Secretary,' Lieutenant (j.g.) Jones replied. 'They are both nearly alone in the world, and they . . . sort of cling to each other.'

'Dolling,' the secretary said, 'in the strictest confidence, of course, I vant to tell you that your government hopes dey keep clinging together like flypaper.'

'Why should our government be interested in the romantic attachment between an obscure student nurse and an English midshipman . . . an orphan midshipman, at that?'

'I mentioned before, you were listening? I said that dot the fellow vot owns duh base at Herstead-on-Heath was His Grace Hugh Percival, Duke of Folkestone Viscount Wemberly, Baron Herstead?'

'Yes, sir.'

'I god news for you, dolling, about dat fellow you been carrying around in duh trunk of your Volkswagen,' the secretary said.

'He's English, of course,' Lieutenant (j.g.) Jones replied. 'So it would logically follow that he's connected in some way with the Duke of Folkestone. Is that close?'

'Not close enough. He *is* the Duke of Folkestone.'

'My God!' Lieutenant Jones said.

'Just "Your Grace",' the secretary said, 'is vat you normally call him.'

'I don't understand.'

'He's vat you call incognaminous,' the secretary said.

'Incognito, Mr. Secretary,' Admiral Saltee corrected.

'What he said. Nobody knows but a couple of people, now including you.'

'His secret is safe with me,' Lieutenant (j.g.) Jones said.

'Ve know,' the secretary said.

'What is this all about?' Joanne Pauline Jones asked.

'Effery year, as you know, the midshipmen take vat dey call a cruise.'

'Yes, sir.'

'Dey find out about boats.'

'Ships, Mr. Secretary.'

'Look, Saltee, *I'm* the secretary of state. You're just a lousy admiral. Ven I vant expert advice, I'll ask for it. Until I do, you just sit there and try to sober up.' The admiral stiffened and assumed a look of injured dignity which would have been far more convincing had he not hiccuped. The secretary turned to Lieutenant (j.g.) Jones. 'Ged oudt your pencil, dolling,' he said, 'and take notes. I'm going to lay it all oudt for you.'

It took some time, because every detail had been carefully planned, but in just over an hour Lieutenant (j.g.) Jones had all the pertinent details of OPERATION HAPPY SAILOR.

Reduced to its essentials, it was simply a plan to (a) keep Midshipman His Grace Hugh Percival, Duke of Folkestone, Viscount Wemberly and Baron Herstead, happy and (b) to impress upon him how much the United States government appreciated the privilege of being allowed to lease Herstead-on-Heath as a nuclear-submarine supply and maintenance base. The United States government was paying an annual rental of one pound sterling for the base, as the result of an agreement negotiated between the previous duke and Rear Admiral (Upper Half) Casper C. Davies, U.S.N. The negotiations took place in La Maison de Toutes Les Nations in Marseilles, France. The two old salts had met by coincidence there while the American admiral was conducting an investigation *vis-à-vis* making the establishment off limits to U.S. Navy Personnel and the retired English admiral and nobleman was revisiting the scene of some youthful wild oats sowing, in company of Mr. Angus MacKenzie. After a number of toasts to Anglo-American naval camaraderie, Vice Admiral His Grace the Duke of Folkestone had discovered he was without funds to either pay for his rounds of drinks or for other services offered by the establishment.

Wittily paraphrasing that cherished phrase of English literature, 'My Kingdom for a Horse,' the duke had literally bartered away on a lease basis, his baronial property, the port of Herstead-on-Heath, to the U.S. Navy in exchange for a cash advance. In the morning, proving that he was an English gentleman, in or out of his cups, he had honoured the agreement made in the wee hours of the previous morning. The present duke had renewed the lease, on the one-pound-per-annum basis, shortly after assuming his title.

Since the most conservative estimate of the real value of

the leasehold was in the neighbourhood of one million dollars per annum, the United States government was understandably anxious to maintain the status quo.

Hence, Lieutenant (j.g.) Jones learned (she was not told where, of course, or under what circumstances the original negotiations had taken place) of the government's interest in keeping Midshipman Woody Woodburn-Haverstraw happy.

Actually, very little deviation from the procedures long established for foreign midshipmen would be required. Every year at the close of the school year, midshipmen from abroad were given a two-week leave in the United States, during which they were entertained by sponsors recruited among naval academy faculty and other interested personnel. This was followed by a cruise aboard a U.S. Navy man-of-war, which customarily travelled to foreign ports. Another leave was granted in the foreign port, permitting the midshipmen to visit their homes. Finally, they rejoined their ships and sailed back to the United States in time for the fall term at the naval academy.

In this case, Midshipman Woodburn-Haverstraw would spend his two-week leave with his sponsors (Dr. and Mrs. Benjamin Franklin Pierce and Dr. and Mrs. John Francis Xavier McIntyre) in the quaint and bucolic Maine sea-coast village of Spruce Harbor. Other foreign midshipmen, after spending their first leave elsewhere, would join together at Spruce Harbor. When they were all assembled, they would board at Spruce Harbor the USS *Satyriasis*, a nuclear submarine of the latest model, and sail across (actually under) the broad Atlantic to Herstead-on-Heath. After a tour of those facilities, the midshipmen would be placed on leave to visit their families in Europe and would later rejoin the USS *Satyriasis* for the return voyage to the United States.

It was even customary to send an escort officer along with the midshipmen, to ease their transition from student status to that of supernumerary crewmen aboard the man-of-war and to keep them out of trouble as much as possible.

Lieutenant (j.g.) Jones would serve as the escort officer. It wasn't exactly what she had envisioned was going to happen when Admiral Saltee had gleefully cried 'Anchors aweigh!' at

68

her and told her she was going to sea, but it was an improvement over what the navy had originally planned to do with her over the summer (a series of speeches to women's liberation groups, during which she was expected to extol the manifold opportunities offered by the navy to those of the allegedly gentle sex), and she consoled herself with the knowledge that she would be, in fact, the first skirted naval officer ever to sink beneath the waves aboard a nuclear submarine.

Her orders were simple: 'Whatever makes that dolling boy happy, dolling, do it. Within reason, of course,' the secretary told her.

Lieutenant (j.g.) Jones anticipated no trouble whatever. Woody would, of course, be in seventh heaven just being with Miss Beverly Chambers for two uninterrupted weeks. And certainly, sponsored as he was by two distinguished practitioners of the healing arts and their wives, nothing untoward could possibly happen.

As the briefing was being carried out in the Secretary's Dining Room of the State Department Building, in our nation's capital, another conference, at the highest political level, was being held in the Senate Office Building.

Earlier that same day, Senator J. Ellwood 'Jaws' Fisch (Moralist-Liberal, Calif.) had received a telephone call from, of all places, Spruce Harbor, Maine. The call was, of course, collect (there was no sense throwing money away when one could arrange for the unsuspecting taxpayers to pick up the tab), and it came from the famous gourmet and, more to the point, animal lover, Taylor P. Jambon.

'It's all fixed, Jaws,' Mr. Jambon said. 'There's only one teensy-weensy problem.'

'What's all fixed . . . and will you stop calling me "Jaws" . . . and what's the teensy-weensy problem?'

'Miss Patience Throckbottom Worthington has graciously consented to make at least a half-dozen sixty-second television appeals for funds for the Association of Pup and Pussy Lovers in Earnest, Inc.,' Mr. Jambon said.

'How much is it going to cost us?' the senator inquired.

'You must remember, Jaws, that it is necessary to spend a

69

little bread to make a little bread, as Henry Ford was saying to me just the other day,' Taylor P. Jambon said. 'And it's not us it will cost, but APPLE.'

'How much, Taylor P?' the senator demanded firmly. 'In case you've forgotten, we own APPLE.' Mr. Jambon gave the figure.

'That much?' the senator said, shocked. 'Taylor P., you're out of your gourd. There won't be anything left for the goddamned animals, much less us.'

'Now listen, Jaws,' Taylor P. said firmly. 'That old broad is America's most beloved thespian. I told you before, when she gets on the tube and starts pitching starving puppies and poor little motherless pussies all across the length and breadth of this great land, there won't be a dry eye from Maine to Oregon.'

'You better be right,' the senator replied. 'I didn't get into the animal game to lose my shirt, you know.'

'Trust me, Jaws,' Taylor P. Jambon had replied. 'Believe me, once we get the old hag in the can, the money will roll in by the bucketful.'

'It'll have to, if we're going to pay her that much money,' the senator said. 'You still haven't mentioned the teensy-weensy problem, Taylor P.'

'It's right down your alley,' Taylor P. said. 'All you have to do is figure some way to get Miss Patience Throckbottom Worthington and a camera crew back and forth to Vienna, Austria.'

'Vienna, *Austria?*' the senator replied. 'You mean, the one in *Europe? That* Vienna, Austria?'

'Right.'

'What the hell for?'

'She said that to do a really good job for us, she must be in the right frame of mind, must really *feel* the plight of the pups and pussies.'

'And they don't have any cats and dogs in Maine, is that what you're trying to tell me?'

'She needs, she says, the right *ambience*, the proper *circumjacence.*'

'The proper *what?*'

70

'Circumjacence,' Taylor P. Jambon repeated.

'What the hell is circumjacence? Doesn't she even speak English, for Christ's sake?'

'I think that is English,' Taylor P. Jambon replied. 'But the bottom line, Jaws, is that she goes to Vienna or the deal is off.'

'Then the deal is off. Don't you have any idea how much it would cost to get a camera crew back and forth to Vienna?'

'I figured you could work something out at your end,' Taylor P. Jambon replied.

'Well, you figured wrong,' the senator said firmly.

'Then we have another teensy-weensy problem,' Taylor P. Jambon said.

'Now what?'

'I already signed the contract,' Taylor P. said. 'I don't know how to tell you this, Jaws, but she gets . . . that figure I mentioned . . . whether or not she makes the commercials, and she won't make the commercials unless she can make them in Vienna, Austria.'

'What's with Vienna, Austria? Is she some sort of Wiener schnitzel freak, or what?'

'I don't really know how to put it,' Taylor P. Jambon said.

'Try,' the senator said.

'Well, when I was in to see her, it was time for her bath . . . she's got a broken leg, you know.'

'No, I didn't know,' the senator said. 'But now that I think about it, if she makes these commercials holding herself up on a crutch, it's not a bad idea.'

'My thinking exactly,' Taylor P. Jambon said. 'There's a visual tie-in. Anyway, as I was saying, when they came into the room to give her her bath, they put one of those screens, so you couldn't see in from the hall, and I went out and stood in the hall, you know . . .'

'Get to the point, for God's sake!'

'You're going to have trouble believing this,' Taylor P. said. 'Well, there I was in the hall, and all of a sudden, down the hall comes half-a-dozen Arabs.'

'What do you mean, Arabs?'

'Arabs, like in Arabia. You know, they wear robes, and they got all the oil.'

71

'Go on.'

'A little fat Arab is out in front, and behind him the other ones. The other ones have got a couple of dogs on leashes. And then Miss Worthington wanted to know what was going on.'

'I thought you said they put a screen in front of the door? How could she see what was going on?'

'I screamed, Jaws,' Taylor P. Jambon said. 'You wouldn't believe these dogs. Black as night. White teeth. Yellow eyes. They tried to eat me. I was afraid for my very life.'

'O.K. I've got the picture. There you are in the hospital corridor. Ferocious dogs are trying to eat you, and you're screaming. Then what?'

'Well, when they heard me screaming . . . and then, too, I suppose they heard the fire extinguisher . . . it made a hell of a racket.'

'The fire extinguisher made a hell of a racket? What *fire extinguisher*?'

'The one on the wall. I tried to climb up on it, and it broke off.'

'Go on, Taylor P.,' Senator Fisch said. His effort to keep control was evident in every somewhat sibilant syllable.

'Well, a couple of doctors came running. I'd hate to be their patients, I'll tell you that.'

'Explain yourself,' the senator said.

'Perverse sense of humour. Instead of coming to my aid, instead of offering succour to a fellow human about to be torn limb from limb by the most *awful*-looking, ferocious, evil-smelling dogs I have ever seen, they had hysterics.'

'Hysterics?'

'Two of them. And a nurse. They had to hold each other up to keep from falling down, such was the level of their perverse delight in my tragic situation.'

'And?'

'And then Miss Worthington called out, to see what was going on.'

'And?'

'And one of the doctors . . . can you believe he doesn't even call himself doctor?'

72

'What does he call himself, Taylor P.?' the senator replied, resigned to the obvious fact that Taylor P. Jambon (as, indeed, he should have known from watching his cooking demonstrations on television) was going to reach the point only after having tangentially bounced off all available walls.

'One of them called himself "Hawkeye," and the other called himself "Trapper John," ' Taylor P. Jambon reported. 'Now I ask you, Jaws, what can you expect from a couple of supposed doctors who run around calling themselves vulgar names?'

'Then what, Taylor P.?'

'The one called "Hawkeye" called out to Miss Worthington "not to worry," that it was just . . . so help me God, Jaws, these are his exact words . . . "a couple of playful puppies" who had scared someone. A couple of puppies, indeed! They looked like black polar bears, that's what they looked like.'

'And then?' the senator pursued patiently.

'The one called "Trapper John" shouted that "Hassan had brought them." Hassan was, I decided, the fat little Arab. So then, Miss Worthington called back, "Isn't that dear Boris' little friend?", and Hawkeye called back, "Yes, it is," and she called out, "Is he there?", and Trapper John said, "No, he isn't, so don't try coming out here with your leg in a cast." And she said, "Well, where is he?", and the fat little Arab said, "He's in Paris, getting ready to go to Vienna." You got all that, Jaws?'

'I think so,' the senator replied. 'This all took place before Miss Worthington insisted on going to Vienna, Austria, to shoot the commercials?'

'Right. Interesting coincidence, isn't it?'

'Coincidence, hell. The old bag has got the hots for this Boris, whoever he is. You ever hear of an Arab named Boris?'

'No, I can't say that I have,' Taylor P. Jambon replied, after some thought.

'You don't suppose we could find him and bring him here? That would be a lot cheaper than buying everybody on a camera crew, plus Miss Worthington, a ticket back and forth to Vienna.'

'Actually, Senator,' Taylor P. Jambon said. 'I wasn't thinking of *buying* a ticket.'

'What were you thinking about?'

'Think hard, Jaws. Isn't there some government function in Vienna that's absolutely crying for your contribution to it, some function you can go to, taking a camera crew and Miss Worthington along as staff?'

'I don't know,' the senator replied. 'But that's a good thought.'

'I thought so.'

'I'll have a little chat with C.C.,' the senator replied, 'and get back to you.'

'Call me at the Spruce Harbor Inn,' Taylor P. Jambon said.

Fifteen minutes later, Senator J. Ellwood 'Jaws' Fisch called upon Senator Christopher Columbus 'C.C.' Cacciatore (Ethnic-Democrat, N.J.) at the latter's office.

Senator Cacciatore was a distinguished-appearing solon who peered solemnly at the world through thick rimmed, heavily corrective spectacles perched low on his nose. His nose was slightly bulbous and of a red tinge, a tribute to the Italian-type Chianti wine of which the senator was quite fond and without a glass of which he was seldom found. He was also fond of pasta in all its various sizes and shapes, which fondness was reflected in his rather ample midsection.

A horseshoe-shaped tuft of snow-white hair circled his head above the ears. The top of his rather large and oddly shaped head, however, was as devoid of hair, to coin a phrase, as cue ball. All in all, his general appearance was of a friendly elder relative, say a Godfather.

Senator Cacciatore's office, in the new Senate Office Building, reflected the prestige in which he was held by his fellow members of what has been laughingly called 'the most exclusive club in the world.' A grateful nation, acting through their elected representatives, had seen fit to provide the senator with a suite of offices panelled in the best walnut available and carpeted with the finest product of the weaver's art. His reception room, roughly the size of a handball court and staffed with six receptionists, each behind a solid mahogany desk, opened into his outer (or official) office, which was roughly the size of a basketball court.

Perhaps stung by the accusation that his outer office bore an unfortunate similarity to that of Benito Mussolini* (it was a three-minute walk from the door to Senator Cacciatore's Roman-style desk), the senator had fallen into the custom of conducting business in his inner (or private) office. A mini-suite, barely forty feet by fifty feet, the private office consisted of still another receptionist's area, a sauna bath, a completely equipped kitchen, a combination dining room and 'lounge,' and, of course, a little hideaway complete with desk for the senator himself.

Senator Cacciatore's value to the Senate had little or nothing to do with his knowledge of international affairs, financial matters, the United States Constitution or national defence. There was more than a germ of truth in the allegation made by the senator's critics that his knowledge of these areas could be written inside a small matchbook with a large crayon.

The senator's value to the Senate, the key to the high regard with which he was held by his fellows, and, indeed, to the unquestioned fact that he was one of the most powerful members of the Senate, was based on his duties within the Senate.

Senator Cacciatore chaired the Senate Committee on Internal Operations. This somewhat euphemistically des-cribed committee was the one charged with such things as assigning office space (senators regarded the location and size of their offices as a most important matter of status) and office staff spaces (each civil servant working for a senator occupies, in the quaint cant of the Senate, a 'space.' A senator provided with fourteen 'spaces,' in other words, is authorized fourteen civil servant flunkies of varying degree and rate of compensation). The Senate Committee on Internal Operations was charged, moreover, with 'reviewing'

*The senator, of course, on one hand, as a responsible solon, recognized Benito Mussolini to be a fascist tyrant. On the other hand, however, Signore Mussolini had been Italian and thus obviously couldn't have been *all* bad.

75

senators' expense vouchers to make sure that the expenditures were made in the public interest.

Senators who had been unwise enough to cross Senator Cacciatore had quickly learned that this meant, for example, that they could expect to pay for the expense of going home to mend political fences themselves. Those who enjoyed Senator Cacciatore's favour, on the other hand, could turn in their expense vouchers in the sure knowledge that a cheque from the U.S. Treasury would soon arrive to compensate them for money spent, no matter with what gay abandon, while they were about the nation's business.

Another of Senator Cacciatore's functions was overall supervision of Senate ad hoc committees. After a number of irresponsible journalists, whose yellow journalism threatened the very fibre of the democratic system, had written at some length about what they called 'criminal abuses' in the 'junketing* outrage,' Senator Cacciatore, calling a press conference, had announced that junkets would be, henceforth and forevermore, a thing of the past.

'Junketing,' he said, 'is now dead. I ask you to join with me in closing the door on it forever and looking only to the future.'

A Senate ad hoc committee, of course, was a horse of a different colour. Who (even Howard K. Smith) would dare question the constitutional right of the Senate to form ad hoc committees? And who (even William F. Buckley) would dare question the right of an official ad hoc committee of the United States Senate to journey, say, to Tokyo, Japan, to study at firsthand the working conditions of geisha girls?

It was with this business of forming ad hoc committees in mind that Senator J. Ellwood 'Jaws' Fisch appeared, literally hat in hand, at the offices of Christopher Columbus Cacciatore.

*A junket, for the politically naive, is a journey undertaken at the taxpayers' expense by congressmen when they have nothing else to do and generally means a trip to places like Paris, France, or the island of Bali, often accompanied by members (generally female) of the congressman's staff. The best 'junkets' (such as those to Paris) go to those solons whom the voters have not seen fit to return to office. They are known, to the cognoscenti, as 'lame-duck consolation junkets.'

'Get to the point, Fisch,' Senator Cacciatore said, once Senator Fisch had been ushered into his inner office and the door was discreetly closed. 'What's in the box?'

'I just happened, Senator, to come across a few bottles of extra-special Chianti while passing through a liquor store, and I thought you might be gracious enough to accept them as a small token of my admiration and esteem.'

The senator pried the crate open, pulled out a raffia-wrapped bottle of the very best quality Chianti, examined it critically, and then reached up and pinched Senator Fisch on the cheek.

'You're a good boy, Fisch,' he said. 'Not too bright, but your heart is in the right place.'

'I'm glad you're pleased,' Senator Fisch said.

'Now, Fisch, what can Christopher Columbus Cacciatore do for you?'

'Certainly, Senator, you're not suggesting that there is any connection between a few bottles of wine between old friends . . .'

'Old *acquaintances*, Fisch. Maybe fellow public servants. But don't presume. We're not old friends.'

'No offence intended,' Fisch said.

'It didn't happen,' Senator Cacciatore replied. 'Now, Fisch, what can I do for you?'

'I want to go to Austria,' Fisch blurted, 'and take a couple of people with me.'

'*Austria?*' Senator Cacciatore asked. 'Austria?'

'Yes, sir,' Senator Fisch said.

'Absolutely out of the question. Positively no,' Senator Cacciatore said. 'And I think I should tell you, Fisch, for your own information, that you've got one hell of a nerve coming in here and asking me, Senator Christopher Columbus Cacciatore himself, something like that. If you're smart, young man, you'll be pretty careful with your expense vouchers in the future.'

CHAPTER EIGHT

Senator J. Ellwood 'Jaws' Fisch stared at Senator Christopher Columbus Cacciatore with shock and horror and some confusion in his eyes. He had obviously angered the beloved chairman of the Senate Committee on Internal Operations. How, he had no idea. But he had. That was a frightening prospect. Those who angered Senator Cacciatore were likely to find themselves conducting their Senate business out of offices located in the basement of the Department of Interior, rather than in the Senate Office Building, and typing their own letters on portable typewriters, rather than having them typed on the latest IBM electrics by highly paid secretaries.

'Senator,' Fisch said, 'there must be some misunderstanding!'

'There's no misunderstanding, Senator,' Senator Cacciatore said, with icy, menacing courtesy. 'You're not trying to tell me I'm losing my hearing, are you?'

'No, sir, of course not, Senator Cacciatore.'

'With my own two ears, Fisch,' Senator Cacciatore said, 'I heard you say that you wanted to go to Austria. You *did* say you wanted to go to *Austria*, didn't you?'

'Yes, sir, I said that,' Senator Fisch admitted.

'Well, there you have it!' Senator Cacciator said. 'Now get out of here, before I forget that I'm a U.S. Senator and let you have a good one in the chops.'

Fisch was twice desperate. Not only were all his senatorial privileges from expense vouchers to office space (not to mention free postage and reduced rates in the senatorial barbershop), in great danger, there was still the business about getting Patience Throckbottom Worthington and a camera crew back and forth to Vienna. Unless he came up with some way to stick the taxpayers for it, he was going to have to pay for it himself, a prospect he found quite painful. Gathering his courage, he straightened his shoulders.

'What exactly do you have against Austria, Senator?' he asked.

'You're asking *me*, Christopher Columbus Cacciatore, what I have against Austria?'

'Yes, sir, Senator, that's what I'm asking.'

'I'll tell you,' the Senator replied. 'And I'm surprised you don't already know. They shoot kangaroos and make shoes out of them, that's what I have against Austria.'

'I beg your pardon?' Senator Fisch replied.

'Certainly,' Senator Cacciatore said. 'I know what it's like. I get a little gassy myself sometimes.'

'I mean, sir, I didn't quite understand that.'

'What's to understand? I told you. Those savages run around shooting innocent little kangaroos and make shoes out of them.'

'Kangaroos?'

'Yes, kangaroos,' the senator replied, somewhat impatiently. When Fisch still stared at him in visible confusion, he held his hands up under his chin and jumped around the room. 'Kangaroos,' he repeated. 'Whatsamatter with you, Fisch, you don't like animals? Maybe it's all right with you that those lousy Austrians spend all their time shooting down innocent kangaroos?'

'Senator,' Fisch said, 'I'll have you know that I am a founder and member of the board of APPLE, Inc.'

'What the hell is Apple Ink?' the senator replied. He stopped bouncing around the room but still held his hands together and under his chin. Truth to tell, he did not look unlike a mature, rather portly kangaroo.

'Association of Pup and Pussy Lovers in Earnest,' Senator Fisch replied. 'Our beloved founder and president is Taylor P. Jambon.'

'The famous gourmet? That Taylor P. Jambon?'

'One and the same, sir,' Senator Fisch replied, with quiet pride.

'You don't say?' Senator Cacciatore replied. 'Isn't that interesting? Taylor P. Jambon is Mrs. Cacciatore's next-to-favourite man.'

'After yourself, of course,' Senator Fisch said smoothly.

'No, as a matter of fact, after Boris Alexandrovich Korsky-Rimsakov, the world's greatest opera singer,' the senator replied. 'But we're getting off the subject. What has all this to do with Austria?'

'Might I ever so respectfully suggest that you're just a teensy-weensy, itsy-bitsy mistaken, Senator?'

'Watch yourself, Fisch. I've got a lot of seniority on you, you know.'

'What I was going to suggest, sir, ever so respectfully, is that you have the wrong country.'

'Let me tell you something, Fisch,' Senator Cacciatore said. 'I get my facts from the same man whose name you keep dropping.'

'Sir?'

'Where do you think I heard about the poor kangaroos? And what those lousy Austrians are doing to them? Taylor P. Jambon, that's who. On his weekly television show, "Glorious Gluttony". He gives little talks while stirring things. We always listen to his show while we're waiting for Lawrence Welk. You got to keep up culturally, you know.'

'What I'm suggesting, Senator . . .' Senator Fisch began, but was interrupted.

'When Mrs. Cacciatore and me heard what Taylor P. Jambon said about what those lousy, cold-blooded Austrians are doing to the innocent kangaroos, Fisch, it broke us up. We just sat there and couldn't even enjoy the accordion solo on "Lawrence Welk". I couldn't even see it, the way I was crying.'

'I know what they're doing to the kangaroos is terrible, Senator, but . . .'

'But what? You're not going to stand there and try to excuse it, are you?'

'Senator, I stand with you in condemnation of what the Australians are doing to the kangaroos.'

'So why do you want to go there and throw the American taxpayers' hard-earned money around on a bunch of kangaroo slaughterers?'

'Senator,' Fisch said, carefully, 'I don't think it's the Austrians who are being beastly to the kangaroos.'

'So now you're calling Taylor P. Jambon, famous gourmet and animal lover, a liar, is that it?'

'Perhaps it was a little noisy in your TV room, sir,' Fisch said.

'What sort of an accusation is that?'

'What I'm saying, Senator, is that Taylor P. Jambon was talking about the Australians, not the Austrians.'

'There's a difference?' Senator Cacciatore asked. Geography was not one of his strong points.

'Oh, yes, sir,' Senator Fisch said.

'Like what?'

'Australians, the ones who are so beastly to the dear little kangaroos, wear Smokey the Bear hats pinned up on the side. They're sort of English. Austrians, on the other hand, wear funny little hats with a brush on the side and short leather pants.'

'You don't say?' Senator Cacciatore replied, absolutely fascinated.

'The Austria *I'm* talking about, Senator, is the one with the beer and Johann Strauss.'

' "The Blue Danube?" ' Senator Cacciatore replied.

'Right, Senator. "The Blue Danube" and Wiener schnitzel. *That* Austria.'

'Well, why didn't you come right out and say so?' Senator Cacciatore said somewhat sharply. 'I'm a busy man, Fisch, I've got better things to do than sit around all day making idle chatter with you.'

'And what we want to do in Austria, Senator,' Senator Fisch went on, having just been struck with the first original idea he'd had since junior high school, 'is make television appeals for poor and abused animals. Pups and pussies *and kangaroos.*'

'You got to go to Austria to do that? They don't make commercials in New York no more?' He paused, and Senator Fisch opened his mouth to reply, but before the words could get past his magnificent choppers Senator Cacciatore had an additional thought. 'Tell you what I'm going to do, Fisch,' he said. 'I'm going to have a word with one of the boys, and you can make your commercials right her in the Senate's TV studio. It's for a good cause, so there will be no charge.'

'Well, that's very kind of you, Senator, and I certainly appreciate it, but . . .'

'But what? Don't knock it until you're tried it. The way they got it fixed, it looks like you're in an office in sight of the Capitol Building. It's a picture on the wall, of course, but the dummies watching the tube don't know that. And what could be more inspiring?'

'Miss Patience Throckbottom Worthington is involved, Senator,' Fisch said.

'Miss Patience Throckbottom Worthington . . . the actress . . . *that* Patience Throckbottom Worthington?'

'Yes, sir.'

'She is one of my favourite stars of stage, screen and television,' the senator said. 'A lady of the old school. They don't make them like that no more.'

'No, sir, they don't,' Senator Fisch agreed. 'Well, when Mr. Jambon approached Miss Worthington asking her to make our television appeals for APPLE . . .'

'Taylor P. Jambon himself asked Patience Throckbottom Worthington herself?'

'Yes, sir.'

'Maybe I've misjudged you, my boy,' Senator Cacciatore said. 'Anyone who walks in here with a case of five-ninety-eight-a-bottle Chianti and who knows both Taylor P. Jambon and Patience Throckbottom Worthington can't be as dumb as you look. Was your mother maybe Italian, Fisch?'

'No, sir,' Fisch said. 'I'm sorry she was not.'

'Maybe somebody's got a little secret, way back, you know what I mean?'

'As I was saying, Senator . . .'

'Maybe your grandmother went for a ride on a gondola in Venice,' the senator went on. 'You know how it goes. A bottle of wine, the moon. Those thing happen. We Italians are irresistible, you know.'

'Miss Worthington graciously offered to make our television appeals for us,' Fisch said.

'You can tell by just looking at her what a sweet, kind,

gracious lady she is. There's Italian blood in her, I'll bet my life on it.'

'I'm sure there is,' Fisch said. 'But there's just one teensy-weensy problem.'

'Like what?'

'Miss Worthington says that to get the right feel in the commercials, she has to make them in Vienna.'

'Rome, I'd understand. Venice would speak for itself. Maybe even Naples. But Vienna?'

'They're sad commercials, Senator.'

'Got you!' Senator Cacciatore said. 'I should have thought of that.'

'So our little problem is how to get Miss Worthington and a camera crew to Vienna. At as little expense to APPLE as possible, of course.'

'Naturally,' Senator Cacciatore said and paused thoughtfully.

'I hoped that you could find it in your heart to help us, Senator,' Fisch went on. 'Help us and the poor kangaroos.'

'Stand up, Fisch,' Senator Cacciatore said sternly. Senator Fisch assumed a position which will be remembered by those who have worn their country's uniform at 'attention'. That is to say, he stood as erect as possible, held his hands at his sides, his thumbs lined up with the seams in his trousers, and stared straight ahead. So standing, he looked directly above Senator Cacciatore (who stood, of course, only five-foot-five in his Earth shoes) and into the face of King Victor Emmanuel of Italy, whose photograph hung on the senator's wall beside that of Senator Edward M. Kennedy.

'Your country calls, Senator,' Senator Cacciatore said, solemnly. 'From this moment forward, you are chairman of the Senate Ad Hoc Committee to Investigate the Mistreatment of Kangaroos and Other Innocent Beasts.'

'Thank you, sir.'

'On your way out, Fisch, tell the girl to fix things with the air force.'

'Thank you, sir.'

'Tell her to tell the air force and the State Department that

83

Senator Christopher Columbus Cacciatore himself is personally interested in your ad hoc committee.'

'You're a great and compassionate man, Senator,' Senator Fisch said, sort of choked up.

'Yeah, I know,' Senator Cacciatore said. In a sudden burst of emotion, he stood on his tiptoes, grabbed Senator Fisch by the shoulders, and kissed him on each cheek. 'You get a chance sometime, kid,' he said, 'ask your grandmother if she's ever been to Italy.'

Senator Fisch returned to his office, poured himself a stiff drink, and then telephoned the good news to Mr. Taylor P. Jambon at the Spruce Harbor Inn.

Taylor P. Jambon was delighted with the news about the air force jet which had been placed at their disposal and with what he called the 'unexpected bonus'.

'What unexpected bonus is that, Taylor?'

'The kangaroos, dummy,' Taylor P. replied. 'Boy, I wonder why I didn't think of them for the APPLE campaign? I did a splendid appeal for them on my television show, "Glorious Gluttony".'

'Taylor, I don't think there's many homeless, friendless kangaroos in America.'

'I know that, Jaws, and you know that, but the suckers won't know that. I'll be in touch.'

No sooner had Senator Fisch replaced his telephone in its cradle than it rang again. He pushed the intercom button and had a word with his secretary. 'Inez, I told you, no calls. I'm meditating.'

'It's Senator Cacciatore, Senator. He said it's urgent.'

'Put him through! Put him through!' Senator Fisch said. He had a sudden sinking feeling that something had gone wrong, that perhaps Senator Cacciatore had changed his mind.

'Good afternoon, Senator,' Senator Fisch said into his telephone, oozing charm. 'How good of you to call me!'

'That's not all, Fisch,' Senator Cacciatore said. 'Boy, have I got good news for you!'

'Oh, really?'

'What would you say if I told you that the official U.S.

Senate Ad Hoc Committee to Investigate the Mistreatment of Kangaroos and Other Innocent Beasts has a new Chairman?'

'I'm sure, Senator, that if you have appointed a new chairman, you had your reasons.'

'I myself, Senator Christopher Columbus Cacciatore, have assumed the helm and will guide the committee wherever in the wild world, specifically to Vienna, our duty takes us.'

'Splendid!' said Senator Fisch loyally but without much evident enthusiasm.

'You want to know why?' Senator Cacciatore said.

'If you could tell me without compromising our national security,' Fisch replied.

'I called Mrs. Cacciatore, Fisch. I wanted to tell her that I'd been in a position to help both the abused kangaroos and Miss Patience Throckbottom Worthington.'

'I understand, sir.'

'Mrs. Cacciatore shares my belief that Miss Worthington is a saint. She never misses one of her TV programmes.'

'I see.'

'So I figured she'd want to know, you understand?'

'Yes, sir.'

'So then I told her how I was able to be of service. The air force jet to Vienna, I mean. And you know what, Fisch . . . talk about casting bread on the waters . . .'

'Yes, sir?'

'Guess who's going to sing in Vienna, Fisch?'

'I really have no idea,' the senator replied.

'I'll give you a little hint. There was a special bulletin of the Boris Alexandrovich Korsky-Rimsakov Fan Club.'

'I'm afraid that's not much help, Senator,' Fisch said.

'You do know, Fisch, don't you, who Boris Alexandrovich Korsky-Rimsakov is?'

'Certainly!' Fisch said firmly. Actually he had no idea at all, his musical tastes leaning towards Alice Cooper and Mel Tormé.

'Then guess who's going to give a special *performance magnifique* at the Vienna Opera?'

Senator Fisch thought long and hard. The only Italianate

singer he could think of was Frank Sinatra, and he didn't think Old Blue Eyes was big in the opera department. It was a time, the senator realized, when silence was the better part of valour. He sat there silently.

'The Maestro himself!' Senator Cacciatore said. 'That's who!'

'Splendid!' Fisch said. 'Smashing!'

'So I figured, what the hell, Fisch, all work and no play makes the senator a dull boy, you know? Combine a little pleasure with business, right?'

'Absolutely, Senator,' Senator Fisch replied. 'You took the words right out of my mouth.'

'Mrs. Cacciatore and me will see you in Vienna, Fisch,' Senator Cacciatore said. '*Ciao, bambino.*'

The line went dead.

CHAPTER NINE

Midshipman His Grace Hugh Percival, the Duke of Folkestone arrived at Spruce Harbor, Maine, in what the navy chose to refer to as a POV. POV stand for privately owned vehicle, and the POV in question was the Volkswagen bug owned by Lieutenant (j.g.) Joanne Pauline Jones, U.S.N.

There were two signs making reference to His Grace's presence in the quaint and bucolic seaport village. An oilcloth affair, of the kind used by politicians, strung between telephone poles carried the simple message 'WELCOME HOME, WOODY!'

While a patient at the Spruce Harbor Medical Center, Woody Woodburn-Haverstraw had made a lot of friends, the most notable of whom of course was Miss Beverly Chambers, a student nurse at the institution.

And on the sign before the Finest Kind Medical Clinic & Fish Market, one of those with movable letters and normally used to advertise such things as fresh clams and cut-rate tonsilectomies, the proprietors of that establishment, Hawkeye Pierce and Trapper John McIntyre, had done what they thought should be done to make Woody's escort officer feel welcome.

Woody had often spoken of Lieutenant Jones to the two healers, and they, unabashed and even rather belligerent male chauvinists, had simply presumed that Lieutenant Jones was of the male persuasion. Thus the Finest Kind Medical Clinic & Fish Market's sign, a twenty-by-thirty-foot affair, surrounded by flashing lights of many colours, read

FINEST KIND MEDICAL CLINIC & FISH MARKET
WELCOMES
LT. (j.g.) JOHN PAUL JONES
FATHER OF THE U.S. NAVY

'Oh, I say, Joanne, look at that!' Woody said. He was a tall, rather thin, blond-headed young man. 'Hawkeye and

Trapper John have got rather the wrong idea about you, haven't they?'

'Who are Hawkeye and Trapper John?' Lieutenant (j.g.) Joanne Pauline Jones, U.S.N., asked. She was not very pleased with the sign.

'You'll like them,' Woody said. 'They're really my best friends in all the world.'

Although fiery tongs could not have ripped the admission from her lips, Lieutenant (j.g.) Jones was as vulnerable to curiosity as any other member of her sex.

'What does that mean? Medical Clinic and Fish Market?'

'Why, just what it says. They sell fish, rather good fish, too, as you will find out, and they treat people.'

'They are doctors, these people?'

'Finest kind,' Woody said.

'What's their relationship with the chief of surgery of the Spruce Harbor Medical Center?' That distinguished luminary, according to Lieutenant (j.g.) Jones's travel orders, was Woody's official sponsor.

'Rather good, I would say,' Woody replied, making his little joke. 'Much mutual admiration, that sort of thing.' It was English humour, and as such sailed right over Lieutenant (j.g.) Jones's pretty little head.

'Make the next right,' Woody ordered, 'and you'll see the Spruce Harbor Medical Center. When I spoke with Dr. Pierce, he said to park where it says "reserved for the Internal Revenue Service".'

'He said what?'

'That's his private parking place,' Woody explained. 'When he put his own name up, other people were always stealing his place. But with the IRS sign up, nobody dares.'

As it happened, when the Volkswagen bug rolled up to the Spruce Harbor Medical Center, the chief of surgery was in conference with Richard J. Wilson, M.D., in the former's office. Dr. John Francis Xavier McIntyre and Esther Flanagan, R.N., normally co-conferees at this time of day, were still on duty.

In theory, Dr. McIntyre was delivering himself a lecture on some fine points of technique required of nurses func-

88

tioning in the operating room to a class of student nurses (among whom, incidentally, was Miss Beverly Chambers), and so the records of the Spruce Harbor Nursing School would indicate.

In practice, however, what really happened was that as soon as Dr. McIntyre (or Dr. Pierce, in his turn) opened his mouth, Nurse Flanagan would interrupt:

'What the doctor really means to say, girls,' she would begin, which was the cue for the physician-lecturer to sit down and assume a look of studied agreement while Nurse Flanagan delivered the lecturer. He could tell when the lecture was over, because then Nurse Flanagan would turn to him and deliver her tag line.

'We're all grateful to you, Doctor, for giving us of your valuable time and wide experience, and we hope that you will soon again find the time to spare from your many activities to be with us again.

She would then place her hands before her and make a clapping gesture, which was the cue for the girls to applaud politely.

It was an important, perhaps indispensable, facet of the practise of medicine, but Hawkeye Pierce was just as happy that it was Trapper John's turn to 'lecture' and he could sit in his office, martini in hand, peering through the lens of a telescope at his unsuspecting fellow Spruce Harborians.

He swung the telescope from anatomical study (a couple on a sailboat were exchanging some rather enthusiastic physical manifestations of mutual respect and admiration to the mistaken belief that being in the middle of Spruce Harbor afforded them unbroken privacy) and turned it to what in the army would be known as terrain reconnaissance.

'Hark!' he cried to Dr. Wilson. 'A navy bug with Annapolis tags!'

'Excuse me, Doctor?' Doctor Wilson asked.

'Doctor,' Hawkeye said, 'please present my compliments to Nurse Flanagan. Tell her that Miss Chambers is needed in the Internal Revenue Service parking lot immediately in the interest of hands-across-the-sea.'

'Student Nurse Chambers is needed immediately in the

interest of hands-across-the-sea,' Dr. Wilson repeated. The one thing he had learned here was never to question the chief of surgery. The answers he got when he did so only served to deepen his confusion.

'Or perhaps, under the table,' Dr. Pierce said. 'Be quick about it, Wilson!' He stepped to the French doors leading from his office, opened them, and then turned. 'Come along, Alfred,' he said.

Alfred, who had been lying, minding his own business, in the corner of the office, raised his head, cocked it, and looked at his master with mild interest.

'I'm sorry to wake you, Old Top,' Hawkeye said in a quite credible mimicry of the peculiar speech pattern of the English aristocrat, 'but a countryman of yours has just arrived, and I do think you should pop outside and say hello to him.'

Alfred rose, slowly and with great dignity, to his feet and, swinging his already monstrous tail from side to side, followed Hawkeye out of his office and onto the lawn.

It had been love at first sight between the dog and Dr. Pierce. They had met in the hospital corridor some time before, when the animals had been delivered by His Royal Highness Prince Hassan ad Kayam. He had sniffed once or twice at Dr. Pierce's legs and then immediately lay down at his feet. He had shown no interest whatever in the activities of his brothers, who were playfully trying to get Mr. Taylor P. Jambon down from his perch on a wall-mounted fire extinguisher.

Mr. T. Alfred Crumley, administrator of the Spruce Harbor Medical Center, had, of course, come running when word had reached him that three black bears were on the premises, apparently determined to eat Mr. Taylor P. Jambon.

By the time he got to the scene, however, Nurse Flanagan and Dr. Trapper John had, not without great effort, managed to remove their new canine companions from the premises. The so far unnamed Scottish wolfhound who had sniffed Dr. Pierce, however, refused to leave. He just went limp. Dr. Pierce tried twice and failed to move him by brute strength. It was like trying to pick up a one-hundred-fifty-pound wet noodle, and it quickly became apparent to Dr. Pierce that the only way they were going to be able to get the animal out of the hospital against his wishes was to roll him onto a stretcher, something, considering the dignity of the healing profession generally, he was unwilling to do.

As soon as Mr. Taylor P. Jambon had been calmed down (he had been on the edge of hysteria and had only recovered control of himself when Dr. Pierce had loudly announced that what he obviously needed was an enema), Mr. T. Alfred Crumley had turned to the dog.

'Now, Doctor Pierce,' he said in righteous indignation, 'about that beast . . .'

The dog, on hearing Mr. Crumley's voice, had suddenly jumped to his feet. The hair on his back, from his ears down to the tip of his tail, rose. His lips curled back, exposing enormous teeth. A bloodcurdling growl came from his throat.

Inspiration struck Dr. Pierce. 'Watch it, Crumbum,' he said. 'I don't think Alfred likes you.'

'Alfred?' Mr. Crumley said. '*Alfred?* That's *my* name.'

'No kidding?' Dr. Pierce said. 'What an interesting co-incidence! Sit, Alfred!'

Alfred the dog obediently sat on his haunches, still showing Alfred the administrator most of his teeth.

'Doctor,' T. Alfred Crumley said, 'certainly you will agree that, for purposes of sanitation and other reasons, that . . . that . . . that . . .'

'You're going to hurt Alfred's feelings, Crumbum,' Hawkeye replied. 'I'm not sure that would be a good idea.'

'. . . your dog . . .' Mr. Crumley went on.

'Alfred, you mean?'

'Alfred cannot be permitted to roam the corridors of this hospital,' Mr. Crumley went on.

'Right you are,' Hawkeye replied. 'Alfred will never leave my office, which we will enter through the French doors.'

'He can't stay in your office, either!' Crumley said.

'You tell him that,' Dr. Pierce said. 'I'm not sure he'd listen to me.'

Momentarily defeated and mustering what dignity he could, Alfred the administrator went one way down the

91

corridor while Alfred the dog and his master went the other. He entered the office of the chief of surgery, circled it twice, sniffing all the while, found a corner with a pleasing aroma, and lay down, his head between his paws, looking with adoration at Dr. Pierce.

He seemed to have an uncanny sense of the rules. He was not permitted to leave the office to go into the hospital and never tried to. Within two days, he understood who was permitted in Dr. Pierce's office and who was not, and it was no longer necessary to bolt the door against the uninvited presence of Mr. Crumley, who would no more have attempted to swim the Atlantic.

It was not, of course, Dr. Pierce's intention at first to have the dog accompany him on his daily journey to the hospital. The dog, like other dogs, would make his home at the home of his master. Alfred, however, immediately displayed a certain character failing. While he permitted Mrs. Pierce to feed him, and, indeed, even displayed a certain affection for her when Dr. Pierce was at home, he immediately revealed a mistaken concept of his role as protector of the family. He somehow formed the notion that Mrs. Pierce harboured evil intentions towards the Pierce children and was just waiting for Dr. Pierce to get out of sight before attacking them.

This became apparent on the very first (and as it turned out, only) morning when Alfred was left behind to guard home and hearth while Hawkeye went off at 5:30 A.M. to meet a schedule 6:00 A.M. rendezvous with a gall bladder.

At 6:30, Mrs. Pierce, in her role as a wife and mother, attempted to wake two of her offspring for breakfast. Alfred met her at their bedroom door with bared teeth and one of his unforgettable growls. By that hour, of course, Dr. Pierce was already in the operating room and unreachable, so Mary Pierce had to wait, in mingled rage and terror (dogs *did* eat children; she had read that somewhere), until the Pierce offspring, in their own good time, woke and came down for breakfast with Alfred trailing along behind.

He was no longer growling. He seemed happy and sat by the table while the children ate and Mary Pierce rehearsed

92

the speech her husband would get on his return to the bosom of his family. After breakfast the children went out to play.

For reasons their mother could not quite comprehend, but which were quite clear to them, it seemed to be a splendid idea to see how deep a hole could be washed in the lawn by spraying it with the water hose turned on full force.

When Mary Pierce, seeing the hole and the mud running down the picture window, rushed from the house with the intention of exercising a little motherly authority and discipline, Alfred got the notion that this crazy woman was about to viciously assault the little darlings Hawkeye had left in his care.

He stepped between her and the children and showed his teeth. She slid to a halt on the wet grass, whereupon (apparently in the belief that this was the traditional canine gesture of submission) Alfred put one of his enormous (and rather muddy) paws on her middle and then bent down and licked her face.

Delighted to see that she had joined in their happy frolic, the Pierce offspring then playfully turned the hose on Mommy.

When Dr. Pierce arrived at his office, still in his surgical greens, and answering the telephoned summons stating that if he wasn't home within fifteen minutes, he should not come home at all, a somewhat soggy Mary Pierce issued a series of non-negotiable demands. He returned to the hospital fifteen minutes later with Alfred tagging along behind him. Alfred, thereafter, always joined Dr. Pierce whenever he left his home.

It wasn't as much of an inconvenience as it might appear. For one thing, despite his bulk, Alfred moved with a certain grace and with surprisingly little noise. His own garbage can was set aside for him outside the hospital, and the remnants of a cuisine which the patients frankly found somewhat wanting proved to be just the thing for a growing dog. His brother and sister were victuled by the Bide-a-While Pool Hall & Restaurant, Dr. Trapper John McIntyre and Nurse Flanagan taking turns running down there in the swamp buggy for remnants from that institution's dining room.

To everyone's surprise, and Mary Pierce's barely concealed fury, the dog presented to Dr. McIntyre fell instantly in love with Mrs. McIntyre and followed her around much as Alfred followed Hawkeye around. Lucinda McIntyre promptly dubbed her pet 'Wolf', which quickly became 'Wolfie' and ultimately 'Wolfie-Baby', for he was, as Lucinda pointed out to a somewhat-less-than-enthusiastic Mary Pierce, nothing more than a darling baby.

The bitch given to Nurse Flanagan was instantly installed in the suite of rooms Esther Flanagan occupied in the student nurses' dormitory. She seemed to fit the name 'Duchess' both because she was the gift of a duchess and because she had a certain ducal bearing. Gentlemen callers upon the student nurses quickly learned that it was far better to present large bones to their ladies than boxes of candy. Bones, plural, because the student nurses' dormitory was already the residence of Wee Black Doggie, given to Miss Chambers by Mrs. Angus MacKenzie.

With Wee Black Doggie and Duchess in residence, as Nurse Flanagan quickly began to tell concerned parents, their daughters were safer than they would have been at home. Nurse Flanagan chose to believe 'her girls' that young gentlemen discovered within the dormitory had not been invited. Invited or not, with Duchess and Wee Black Doggie patrolling the corridors, tales of young men in the dormitory quickly became faint memories of the olden days.

Lieutenant (j.g.) Joanne Pauline Jones pulled her POV into the parking space with the neatly lettered sign reserving it for the use of the Internal Revenue Service, and as soon as it had stopped, Midshipman His Grace Hugh Percival, the Duke of Folkestone jumped out.

'Hiya, Woody!' Hawkeye Pierce shouted and wrapped his arms around the young nautical gentleman. Alfred sat back on his haunches and barked, somehow sensing that this was a happy occasion.

Turning to quiet the dog, Hawkeye for the first time saw Lieutenant (j.g.) Jones. She was in civvies, and he had no way of telling that she was a naval officer about her country's business. All he saw was a young, well-stacked blonde lady.

'Woody!' he said. 'You really are a chip off the old block, aren't you?'

'I beg pardon?' Woody asked.

Hawkeye turned around. Student Nurse Chambers and Dr. Wilson were coming into the parking lot.

'Cancel my last order!' he cried. 'Put her on ice!'

But it was too late. Miss Chambers had seen Midshipman His Grace the Duke of Folkestone. They rushed at one another. Hawkeye stepped quickly to the Volkswagen.

'Duck down on the seat before she sees you,' he said, quickly. 'Maybe his uncle could get away with more than his fair share of well-stacked blondes, but in Spruce Harbor that's a no-no.'

'I beg your pardon?' Lieutenant (j.g.) Jones said indignantly.

'Get down! Get down!' Hawkeye repeated. He had a certain commanding presence, and Lieutenant (j.g.) Jones found herself complying with orders.

There was a rather touching scene of reunion between the duke and the student nurse, and then, finally remembering they were in public, they broke apart.

'Woody, this is Dr. Wilson,' Beverly said. 'Hawkeye's teaching him how to cut.'

'How do you do, sir?' Woody replied, offering his hand. 'And I would like to present my good friend ... where is she?'

'Where's who?' Beverly asked.

'Lieutenant Jones,' Woody said. 'She drove me up. She's our summer-cruise escort officer.'

'Oh, I'm so glad,' Beverly said. She was a great admirer of Lieutenant (j.g.) Jones. She had, after all, smuggled Woody off the Annapolis campus more than once in the trunk of the Volkswagen.

They walked quickly to the Volkswagen. Woody pulled the door open.

'There you are,' Woody said.

'Why is she lying down on the seat?' Dr. Wilson inquired.

'Joanne,' Beverly asked. 'are you sick? If you're sick, I'm sure Dr. Wilson would be happy to take care of you.'

'Perhaps she's just bashful,' Hawkeye suggested helpfully. 'She doesn't look sick to me.'

'And if Hawkeye says you're not sick,' Beverly Chambers said loyally and confidently, 'you have nothing to worry about.'

'You're the one with that funny sigh? The Welcome-Father-of-the-Navy, Fines-Kind-Fish-Market Hawkeye?' Lieutenant (j.g.) Jones said, sounding far more like an angry naval officer than what she looked like.

'At your service, ma'am,' Hawkeye replied, bowing deeply.

'You think that's funny, Slim?' Lieutenant (j.g.) Jones snarled. 'Making fun of female naval officers?'

'How was I supposed to know you were a female?' Hawkeye replied.

Dr. Wilson examined her curiously. 'I could tell right off, Doctor,' he said. 'The minute I laid eyes on her.'

'Drop dead.' Lieutenant (j.g.) Jones said. 'The both of you. And Beverly, would you please tell me where I can find Dr. Benjamin Franklin Pierce, the chief surgeon?'

Beverly did not, of course, reply instantly. Framing a reply was something of a challenge. There was plenty of time for Lieutenant (j.g.) Jones to turn to face Hawkeye and Dr. Wilson again.

'Get your stories straight, you two,' she said. 'I'm reporting you both to Dr. Pierce.'

Dr. Pierce's face took on a strange appearance. He seemed about to burst out in laughter. Dr. Wilson looked at Lieutenant (j.g.) Jones with an even stranger look on his face. It looked quite familiar to Hawkeye, and after a moment it came to him where he'd seen it before. Dr. Wilson was looking at Lieutenant (j.g.) Jones with exactly the same look in his eyes as Alfred the dog had in his eyes when he looked at Hawkeye.

'I think,' Hawkeye said to Lieutenant (j.g.) Jones, 'that he wants you to scratch his ears.'

Lieutenant (j.g.) Jones looked dumfounded. 'Take me to Dr. Pierce!' she said. 'This instant!'

'Permission to speak, ma'am?' Midshipman Woodburn-

Haverstraw asked, in the prescribed manner for a lowly midshipman to speak to an august commissioned officer of the naval service.

This got through to Dr. Wilson.

'I like boats,' he said, 'and things like that.'

'Permission granted,' Lieutenant (j.g.) Jones replied, quite as nautically.

'Anything to do with the sea,' Dr. Wilson said. 'Maybe we could talk about it sometime. You don't happen to be free tonight by any chance, Admiral?'

'Ma'am,' Woody said, 'may I present Dr. Benjamin Franklin Pierce, Fellow of the American College of Surgeons and Chief of Surgey of the Spruce Harbor Medical Center?'

'We could go to the Bide-a-While Pool Hall,' Dr. Wilson pursued. 'They serve lobsters and clams. They even have a fishing net and a steering wheel hanging from the wall. So you'd feel right at home, Admiral.'

'You're kidding,' Lieutenant (j.g.) Jones replied.

'No, I'm not,' Dr. Wilson said. 'Stanley . . . he's the owner . . . bought them at an auction.'

'The Finest Kind Medical Clinic & Fish Market is at your command, Lieutenant,' Hawkeye said. 'What'll it be? A nice tonsillectomy, or a couple of dozen clams?'

'Sir,' Lieutenant (j.g.) Jones said, icily, 'I transfer herewith into your custody for a fourteen-day leave Midshipman Woodburn-Haverstraw, Royal Navy, on temporary duty, U.S. Naval Academy.'

'A pleasure, I'm sure,' Hawkeye said. 'Lieutenant, may I present Dr. Richard Wilson, one of our most promising bachelor physicians?'

At that moment Dr. Trapper John McIntyre and Nurse Esther Flanagan appeared, Nurse Flanagan having somewhat abruptly called off the class in operating procedures in the correct belief that Beverly Chambers had been summoned because Woody had, so to speak, come home.

She wrapped Woody in a motherly hug, then spotted Lieutenant (j.g.) Jones.

'Who,' she demanded, 'is the blonde?'

'I am Lieutenant (j.g.) J. P. Jones, United States Navy,' the lieutenant announced.

'And what's your connection, Lieutenant, with our Woody?'

'I am his official escort officer,' Lieutenant Jones said.

'Well, why didn't you say so?' Esther Flanagan said. 'Welcome aboard, Lieutenant.' She put out her hand. 'Flanagan, Esther B., Lieutenant Commander, Navy Nurse Corps, Retired.'

Somewhat flustered, Lieutenant (j.g.) Jones put out her hand.

'We're about to splice the mainbrace, Lieutenant.' Esther Flanagan said. 'Come along with us.'

'I think it would perhaps be better if I stayed with Woody . . . with Midshipman Woodburn-Haverstraw.'

'What are you, some kind of spoilsport?' Flanagan said. 'You come with us, Lieutenant. You may consider that an order.'

'We could go down to the marina and rent a rowboat,' Dr. Wilson said.

'I'm Trapper John,' that healer announced, 'since no one is going to introduce us.'

'Watch out for him, honey,' Flanagan said. 'If you want to fool around, the only bachelor around here is Wilson, and he's only a lousy resident.'

Midshipman His Grace Hugh Percival, the Duke of Folkestone and Miss Beverly Chambers heard nothing of this. Hand in hand, cheek to cheek, they had disappeared around the corner of the building.

Trapper John looked at Hawkeye. 'I told you I always thought we were in the wrong service,' he said. 'the only escort officer I had in the army had been an all-Army fullback.'

At that moment Alfred the dog, having come to the conclusion that Lieutenant (j.g.) Jones was good people, gave her a friendly little nudge with his nose. Since he was somewhat larger than most dogs, his nose was somewhat higher off the ground than the noses of his fellow canines. The nudge thus touched Lieutenant (j.g.) Jones on a portion of her anatomy where she was not accustomed to be nudged. She stiffened and then resumed walking. Alfred the dog nudged her again.

'How dare you?' cried Lieutenant (j.g.) Jones with all the feminine outrage and naval officer's dignity that she could muster, simultaneously spinning around to, she was quite sure, slap the outrageous Dr. Wilson on his arrogant male chauvinist face. How *dare* he goose a naval officer in the execution of her official duties?

Dr. Wilson was eight feet away. The slap whistled menacingly but harmlessly through the air. Alfred the dog, however, delighted that he finally had captured her attention, reared back on his hind legs, draped his paws over her shoulders, and affectionately lapped her face.

Lieutenant (j.g.) Joanne Pauline Jones began to cry.

CHAPTER TEN

The Spruce Harbor, Maine, International Airfield* is classified as a military auxiliary airfield because the U.S. Coast Guard has had a long-standing deal with the proprietor, one Wrong Way Napolitano, to refuel coast guard aircraft on a reimbursable-in-kind basis.

What this meant was that about once each six months, a coast guard patrol plane or a coast guard helicopter would find itself low on fuel and land at Spruce Harbor International to take on enough gas to get them to what they somewhat less than tactfully referred to as 'a real airport.' The next time a coast guard truck was headed in the direction of Spruce Harbor, a couple of fifty-five-gallon drums of fuel would be loaded aboard to be dropped off to repay that borrowed from Wrong Way. Mr. Napolitano, who had distinguished World War II service as a PFC–radio operator in the U.S. Army Air Corps, felt it was the least he could do for the coast guard. The coast guard had always been willing to come rescue him from the briny deep when his Boston Whaler ran out of gas between his lobster traps, and turnabout was certainly fair play.

Spruce Harbor International Airfield was a military field, dedicated to the service of the armed forces, and could be presumed to have available certain amenities. Among these amenities (an amenity is a pleasant custom), further, could be expected to those dear to the heart of senior military and naval officers, that of 'honours.' When a general or an admiral arrives at a military or naval airfield, he expects far more than having a set of steps rolled up to the aircraft and directions to the gentlemen's rest facility.

*The installation, previously named the Napolitano Crop-dusting Service & Garage, was renamed Spruce Harbor International Airfield by the Spruce Harbor Chamber of Commerce after a DC-3 bound from Bangor, Maine, to Quebec, Canada, had gotten lost and landed by mistake at Mr. Napolitano's place of business.

He expects, at the very least, to be greeted at the door of his airplane by the commanding officer of the facility, the aerodrome officer of the day, a staff car, and, under certain circumstances, by a band, the national colours with an honour guard, and lines of enlisted men standing at attention to have their shoeshines and haircuts examined.

This is, to reiterate, known as 'honours'. Honours are not paid to run-of-the-mill officers (colonels and navy captains down). They have to get off airplanes by themselves and follow the arrows to the gentlemen's. Since it is obviously impractical to have commanding officers, aerodrome officers of the day, and the rest of it standing by to greet an airplane which might contain two sergeants and a chief petty officer, a rather clever little warning code has been established.

As soon as the pilot of a military aircraft carrying a general or flag officer aboard establishes radio contact with the military airfield at which he will land, he announces that aircraft so-and-so has a 'Code Six Aboard.'

This is the signal for the control to telephone the commanding officer's secretary to tell him (or her, as the case may be) to wake the old man up and get him to the airfield; to form the band and the honour guard; and to gather together a sufficient quantity of neatly barbered troops to be inspected.

The announcement that a 'Code Six Is Aboard' serves also to warn the control-tower operator to clear the skies for the arrival of a big shot. Generals and admirals are far too important personages to waste their time holding in the pattern waiting for their turn to land; they are to be given permission to land immediately. Waiting around in the holding pattern is another of the crosses the junior officers have to bear.

Code Six identifies one- and two-star generals and admirals. Code Seven identifies lieutenant generals and certain senior governmental officials, such as senators and congressmen, who, when dealing with the military, are given what is known as 'assimiliated rank'. Senators and congressmen get the same fancy treatment, in other words, as lieutenant generals and vice admirals.

One step above a Code Seven is a Code Eight, which identifies four-star admirals and generals. The only thing that outranks a Code Eight in the honours department is when the pilot is able to identify his aircraft as Air Force One. This means, of course, that the President of the United States is aboard. In ascending order, other cabinet officers, when airborne, have their aircraft identified as Air Force Two (the Vice President); Air Force Three (the Secretary of State); and so on, up through the Secretary of Health, Education and Welfare, who is known as Air Force Sixteen.

All of this background is necessary to explain what happened that memorable morning thirteen days after Midshipman His Grace Hugh Percival, the Duke of Folkestone and Lieutenant (j.g.) Joanne Pauline Jones, U.S.N., came to Spruce Harbor.

Wrong Way Napolitano himself was in the Spruce Harbor tower, a rather windblow structure suspended on surplus poles contributed as a public service by the Maine Telephone Company, access to which was by rope ladder which Mr. Napolitano could (on occasion, such as now) pull up after him, thereby giving him refuge from Mrs. Napolitano, whose temper (on occasion, such as now) was another of Maine's charming legends.

When the radio burst into life, Mrs. Napolitano had finally faced the cold reality that her husband had no intention of coming down from his aerie and that she stood no chance whatever of going up after him, since he had had the foresight, in addition to pulling the rope ladder up after him, to grease the structure's four supporting poles.

He had just settled down for a long session with his collection of *Playboyo Italiano* Magazine. He had a gallon bottle of Chianti wine, a loaf of bread, and a hunk of cheese to sustain him through the hurricane of her rage, which, from long experience, he judged would last at least until noon of the following day. Mrs. Napolitano had chosen not to believe that Wrong Way's low passes over a certain section of the rocky beaches had been nothing more than practice in aerial flight. She had been informed that a group of female college students, nature lovers, had chosen that section of beach to commune with nature and without bathing suits (or other garments) to disturb their vibrations.

'Spruce Harbor International,' the radio said crisply, 'Navy Nine-Two-Three, Code Six Aboard, fifteen miles south-southeast your station. Request approach and landing instructions.'

He stared at the radio for a long minute before picking up the microphone.

'Navy aircraft calling Spruce Harbor,' he replied. 'You sure you got the right place, Mac?'

The Code Six aboard Navy Nine-Two-Three was Rear Admiral (Lower Half) J. Kingswood Saltee, U.S.N. Admiral Saltee was FOICUSNAGCO* and in the execution of his official duties. Word had reached him via a very reliable source (Admiral Reginald C. 'Totter' McSwain, U.S.N., who had been a fellow defensive tackle on the '48 Naval Academy football team) that the Secretary of State, for reasons Admiral Saltee couldn't imagine, had privately expressed doubt that FOICUSNAGCO could handle a certain delicate mission he had been assigned.

'Jake,' Admiral McSwain had said, calling on the scrambler phone, 'delay sneaking the broad aboard. You-know-who with the funny accent knows all about it.'

'I don't know what you're talking about, Totter,' Admiral Saltee had replied.

'Listen to me, Jake,' Admiral McSwain said. 'I just happened to be in the executive steam bath over at the State Department, under a pile of towels, when you-know-who came in. I heard him talking on the phone. He knows all about it, I tell you.'

'All about what?'

'You sneaking some English broad aboard ship,' Admiral McSwain said. 'He doesn't think you'll get away with it, Jake. That means he knows. You want to tell me about it?'

'Totter, I appreciate the call,' Jake Saltee replied.

'Who's the broad for, Jake?' Admiral McSwain pursured.

*Flag Officer in Charge, U.S. Naval Academy Governmental Coordination Office, or FOICUSNAGCO, pronounced Foy-Cus-Nag-Co.

'What exactly *did* you-know-who say, Totter?' Admiral Saltee asked.

'Well, you know, Jake. With that sauerkraut accent, you have a hard time understanding him. The best I could make of it was, "You'd think Saltee would be able to get one lady onto a boat without schlepping up the whole operation, but I have my doubts".'

'He said that, did he?'

'That's what he said,' Admiral McSwain confirmed. 'What are you up to, Jake?'

'I'm sorry, Totter,' Admiral Saltee said, 'you don't have a "Need to Know".'

'You embarrass the navy, Jake, and you can forget about getting to be an Upper Half Rear Admiral.'

'Totter,' Admiral Saltee said, with icy dignity, 'you seem to forget that you're talking to the man who kicked the field goal against Army, winning the game. After, I must point out, you stepped on your shoelace and fell flat on your face on the two-yard line.'

'You're never going to let me forget that, are you?'

'It seems to me that a man who forgot to tie his shoelaces when the honour of the academy was at stake is in no position to talk about duty to me,' Admiral Saltee said.

'That was thirty years ago,' Admiral McSwain said.

'As the twig is bent, Totter,' Admiral Saltee said. 'As the twig is bent.'

'I didn't call to criticize, Jake. I called to offer any assistance that you might require.'

'You really want to help, Totter?'

'You know I do, Jake.'

'Then go back to the steam room and keep your eyes and ears open.'

'I spend so much time in there now I look like a lobster,' Admiral McSwain said.

'We all must expect to make sacrifices during our careers, Admiral Saltee said. 'You get back into the steam room and keep me posted.'

'Aye, aye, sir,' Admiral McSwain had said and broken the connection.

Admiral Saltee hung up the scrambler phone and punched his intercom.

'Yeoman,' he said, 'top priority. Lay on an aircraft for an immediate flight to Spruce Harbor, Maine. The fastest thing in the naval academy's fleet.'

'Aye, aye, sir,' the yeoman said. 'I have to tell you, sir, that the fastest thing available right now is an R-4D.*'

'A gooney bird?' the admiral said. 'Where's all the jet transports?'

'At San Diego Naval Air Station, sir.'

'What are they doing there?'

'We're playing Southern California, sir. I thought you knew.'

'So I did, so I did,' Admiral Saltee replied. 'Well, to quote myself, "We must all expect to make sacrifices during our careers". Have it warmed up. I'm on my way to the airfield.'

'Aye, aye, sir,' the yeoman said.

'Spruce Harbor, Navy Nine-Two-Three, I say again, Code Six Aboard, request approach and landing instructions,' the pilot of Admiral Saltee's gooney bird said now.

Another voice suddenly came over the air, with just a tint of arrogance:

'Spruce Harbor International, this is Air Force Six-Twenty-Six. I have a Code Seven Aboard. As a matter of fact, I have *two* Code Sevens aboard. Request approach and landing instructions.'

'Navy Nine-Two-Three, Spruce Harbor clears you for a direct approach to Runway Number Three-Eight. You are number one to land,' Wrong Way said.

'Spruce Harbor, Air Force Six-Two-Six. I say again I have two Code Sevens aboard. Request permission for immediate approach and landing.'

'Six-Two-Six, wait your turn,' Wrong Way said. 'Nine-Two-Three got here first.'

'That's not the way it works, and you know it. I've got two

---

* R-4D is the navy designation for the Douglas DC-3. It is the navy version of the first really successful transport aircraft. Twin-engined, carrying sixteen to twenty passengers, it travels, presuming a good tailwind, at approximately two hundred miles per hour.

Code Sevens. That lousy Code Six is just going to have to wait.'

'Spruce Harbor, this is Air Force Three,' still another voice said. 'Request immediate approach and landing instructions.'

'Air Force Three, there's a navy gooney bird and an air force Sabreliner ahead of you,' Wrong Way replied. 'You're number three to land. Hold in the pattern.'

'Spruce Harbor, this is Air Force Three. Say again.'

'Hold in the pattern,' Wrong Way replied. 'You're number three to land.'

'Spruce Harbor, are you telling Air Force Three to *hold in the pattern*?' Air Force Three said, showing shocked, outraged disbelief at this outrageous flaunting of all that the bureaucrats and the military hold dear.

'You got it, Charley,' Wrong Way said. 'Navy Nine-Two-Three, the altimeter is one niner niner, the winds are negligible from the north. You are cleared to land.'

'Navy Nine-Two-Three over the outer marker,' the gooney bird said, just a trifle smugly.

'Spruce Harbor,' Air Force Three said, practically shouted. 'We have the Secretary of State aboard!'

'Really?' Wrong Way said. 'Navy Nine-Two-Three, Spruce Harbor. Abort your approach and go around.'

Navy Nine-Two-Three, when it received this message, had already touched down, but orders from the control tower are orders which cannot be disobeyed. The gooney-bird pilot, who had his hands on the throttles to retard them, now shoved them as far forward as they would go. The engines responded, and Navy Nine-Two-Three, quickly gathering speed, soared off into the sky again.

Air Force Six-Two-Six, which had been observing Navy Nine-Two-Three land, whooshed in towards Spruce Harbor International's Runway Number Thirty-eight.

'Air Force Six-Two-Six over the outer marker,' its pilot said, lowering his wheels.

'Air Force Six-Two-Six, Spruce Harbor, go around,' Wrong Way said. 'Air Force Three, you say you have the Secretary of State on board?'

Air Force Six-Two-Six, which had lowered its wheels, flaps and speed brakes, now raised its wheels, retracted the speed brakes, and zoomed off into the wild blue yonder again.

'That is affirmative, Spruce Harbor,' the pilot of Air Force Three said quite smugly. 'Air Force Three has the Secretary of State aboard. May I presume that Air Force Three is number one to land?'

'Hey, Wrong Way,' still another voice said, 'how about chasing those creeps down there away so I can land?'

'That you, Horsey?' Wrong Way replied.

'Me and Hot Lips,' the voice said.

'Air Force Three,' Wrong Way said. 'Spruce Harbor. Hold in the pattern. Spruce Harbor International clears Chevaux Petroleum Number One as number one to land. Welcome to Spruce Harbor, Horsey!'

'Spruce Harbor,' Air Force Three said, 'I must be having trouble with my radio. I could have sworn you just gave landing priority to a *civilian, non-governmental* aircraft!'

'You heard him, Fat Boy,' said the last voice to call in. 'Now get out of the way before I run over you!'

Air Force Three interrupted its landing approach. The huge, glistening intercontinental DC-8 applied power, gained a little altitude and banked to the left. An almost identical (differing only in the paint scheme) DC-8 came in on its tail, dropped its wheels, touched down and rolled to a stop.

Wrong Way Napolitano, reasonably certain that Mrs. Napolitano would not make good her threat to cut his throat with a rusty beer can in the presence of the Reverend Mother Emeritus Margaret H. W. Wilson, of the God Is Love in All Forms Christian Church, Inc., tossed the rope ladder leading to the control tower out the door and clambered down after it.

By the time he reached the ground, the Chevaux Petroleum Corporation aircraft had completed its landing roll, turned around on the runway, and taxied back to the repossessed house trailer which served as the passenger terminus of Spruce Harbor International.

The door opened. Reverend Mother Emeritus Wilson

appeared at the opening. She was wearing her hair differently than Wrong Way remembered. Previously, it had hung down over her shoulders. It was now arranged something like an inverted volcano, rising a good eighteen inches above her head. It was shaped, Wrong Way Napolitano realized, not unlike a bishop's *cappa magna*. There were other similarities to a vested prelate of the church. Reverend Mother Emeritus held in her hand a pole with a curved end, a shepherd's crook, traditional symbol of a bishop. A christian cross, about ten inches in height, hung around her neck, the chain dipping in the valley between her ample bosoms. She was wearing a navy-blue cape, lined in red, over a purple, ankle-length dress. The cape swirled in the wind, revealing that which was printed on the back, in the manner of that printed on the back of prize-fighters' dressing gowns, that is to say, in large, sequined letters.

There was, of course, a cross, signifying her ecclesiastical association. The cross was about four feet high and four inches wide. The word 'REVEREND' was embroidered on the vertical member and the words 'MOTHER' and 'EMERITUS' on the two horizontal cross members. Surrounding this, the words arranged so that they could be read (even though they formed a circle) without twisting one's head, were these words: GOD IS LOVE IN ALL FORMS CHRISTIAN CHURCH, INC., WORLD HEADQUARTERS, NEW ORLEANS, LA.

'Bless you, Antonio!' Reverend Mother Emeritus said, gesturing with her shepherd's crook.

'Hiya, Hot Lips!' Wrong Way shouted back at her. 'Long time no see!'

There was a whirring noise and a flight of stairs unfolded smoothly from the belly of the aircraft. Reverend Mother disappeared from the door only to appear a moment later at the head of the stairs.

'Come, Darling!' she called in her deep and melodious voice, directed to the interior of the aircraft. A large, black Scottish wolfhound, tail wagging, appeared, took one look at Wrong Way, bared its teeth, and started down the stairs after him.

The shepherd's crook in Reverend Mother's hand flashed

out quickly, rapping the animal none too gently on the head. the beast stopped and looked back.

'No, Darling,' Reverend Mother cooed, 'not Wrong Way. He's a friend!'

Another animal appeared, this one a male. He, too, brightened at the sight of Wrong Way, the look coming into his eyes like that of a starving man who comes across a banquet. And he, too, started down the stairs. And he, too, took a rap on the top of his head from Reverend Mother's crook.

'Behave yourself, Beauregard,' she said. 'Wrong Way is Daddy's buddy.'

'Wrong Way!' Daddy said, at that moment appearing at the head of the stairs. 'How dey hanging?'

'Horsey! How are you, buddy?' Wrong Way replied. 'What brings you to Spruce Harbor?'

The man whom Reverend Mother referred to as 'Daddy' and Wrong Way as 'Horsey' was actually Colonel Jean-Pierre de la Chevaux* (Louisiana National Guard), chairman of the board and chief executive officer of the Chevaux Petroleum Corporation, International.

He did not look, truth to tell, very much like the captain of industry and finance that he certainly was. He was wearing a purple nylon flight suit on which were embroidered the somewhat spectacular wings and other insignia of the Cajun Air Force. On his head, to protect its somewhat hairless surface from what Colonel de la Chevaux regarded as the icy winds of Maine, was the uniform hat prescribed for the Supreme Assistant Grand Knight of the Golden Fleece & Social Secretary of the Bayou Perdu Council, Knights of Columbus. This item of uniform had been patterned after the hat worn by officers of the Royal Navy at the battle of Trafalgar.

*The details of Colonel de la Chevaux's spectacular business career, following the discovery of 'the largest pool of natural gas ever to be discovered' on his property in Bayou Perdu, Louisiana, have been chronicled for students of the petrochemical industry and international finance in *M*A*S*H Goes to New Orleans* also in Sphere Books, which is available in the better sort of drugstores, five- and ten-cent stores, and bus terminals.

In his hand he clutched a half-gallon bottle of Old White Stagg Blended Kentucky Bourbon. As he trotted down the stairway, with the Scottish wolfhound trotting along after him. He skilfully twisted the bottle top loose.

'Have a little snort,' he said to Wrong Way.

'Don't mind if I do,' Wrong Way said, taking a healthy pull at the bottle.

'Perhaps just a teensy-weensy taste,' Reverend Mother said, joining them and practically snatching the bottle from Wrong Way's hand. She tipped it up, and there was a steady glug-glug sound lasting a full thirty seconds. 'I always get so thirsty when I fly,' she said, handing the bottle, finally, to Colonel de la Chevaux.

Colonel de la Chevaux, as they say, drank deeply at the only available well and then handed the bottle back to Wrong Way.

'Wrong Way,' he said, glancing up at the sky, through which a gooney bird, a Sabreliner and a DE-8 endlessly circled around the field, 'what the hell is that?'

'Jeez, Horsey,' Wrong Way replied, 'I forgot. Tubby's up there. I better get him down.' He began to clamber back up the rope ladder. As Reverend Mother and Colonel de la Chevaux watched him, there came upon the still air the faint sound of a voice pathetically repeating, over and over, 'Spruce Harbor International, please come in. Spruce Harbor International, please come in.'

CHAPTER ELEVEN

'So, Horsey,' the Secretary of State said minutes later, when he came down the steps of Air Force Three, 'so how's by you?'

'You should have told me you were coming,' Colonel de la Chevaux replied, draping a massive friendly arm around the secretary's shoulders and offering him the bottle of Old White Stagg with the other hand. 'We flew right over Washington, we could have picked you up.'

'I just happened to be in the neighbourhood,' the secretary said, 'so I said, why not drop by and say hello?'

'We're here because our babies were lonely,' Reverend Mother said.

'You should excuse me,' the secretary said. 'I don't think I got that right.'

'Shake hands with nice man,' Reverend Mother said. 'First you, Darling, and then Beauregard.'

Darling, the slightly smaller of the two Scottish wolf-hounds, obediently sat down on her haunches and extended her paw to be shaken. It was a new trick, and Darling really hadn't had the opportunity to polish it. The paw she extended to the secretary struck him in the belly. The wind was knocked out of him, and he put his hands on his somewhat less than perfectly flat abdomen. Beauregard, Darling's brother, then put out his paw, and he wasn't any better at it than Darling. The second extended paw sent the secretary over backwards. Darling and Beauregard, quite understand-ably mistaking this acrobatic motion as the canine gesture of submission, immediately stood over him and licked his face, to show him there were no hard feelings.

'Isn't that sweet?' Reverend Mother cooed. 'They like you, Tubby!'

'And I like them,' the secretary said, without much conviction. 'Nice doggies.'

'You should be flattered,' Reverend Mother went on, pulling Darling and Beauregard off him with her shepherd's crook. 'They don't like everybody.'

'You don't mean it,' the secretary said, getting to his feet and mopping his face, where he had been kissed, with his handkerchief.

'They got one sniff of Hot Lips's fairies and ran them out of International Headquarters,' Horsey de la Chevaux said. 'Right down Canal Street, past the Trade Centre and into the Mississippi River.'

'Horsey,' Reverend Mother said, 'I thought we had agreed we weren't going to bring that up. It was a simple misunderstanding.'

'I forgot,' Horsey said.

'And you also forgot and used that word again,' she said.

'Fairies, you mean?'

'That's what I mean,' she said.

'So, what brings you two to Spruce Harbor?' the secretary asked.

'Darling and Beauregard told me they were lonely for their brothers and sister,' Reverend Mother said. 'So we decided to have a little reunion.'

'With who?' the secretary asked.

'With their brothers and sister, of course,' Hot Lips said.

'You mean there's more?' the secretary said.

'Well, you remember Wee Black Doggie, of course,' Hot Lips said.

'How could I forget?' the secretary replied.

'And then there's Duchess, and Wolfie-Baby, and Alfred the dog,' Hot Lips said. 'It's going to be quite a reunion.'

'*Oy vay!*' the secretary said. He turned and looked over his shoulder. Air Force Six-Two-Six had landed, and the door was open. Senator J. Ellwood Fisch stood in the door.

'*Oy vay!*' the secretary said again. 'Him, I don't need.' A horrible thought crossed his mind. 'Horsey, tell me, he's a friend of yours?'

Horsey looked at Senator Fisch. He shrugged his shoulders and shook his head. 'Never saw him before.'

'Me, either,' Reverend Mother said. 'Although he does

112

look something like my choir director. Maybe they're brothers or something.'

'So, for old times' sake,' the secretary said, 'do me the favour. Don't ask questions. Just get me out of here before that idiot sees me.'

'You got it, Tubby,' Wrong Way replied. He loaded the secretary and Reverend Mother in the cab of his pick-up truck. Horsey, Darling and Beauregard got into the bed, and with a painful clash of gears the truck drove away.

Senator Fisch, who had been ordered by Senator Christopher Columbus Cacciatore to 'see what the hell's going on out there,' ran after the truck, shouting:

'Say there! I'm Senator Fisch! Might I have a moment of your time?'

For some reason, this annoyed Darling and Beauregard. It was all that Horsey could do to keep them in the truck.

As Senator Fisch walked disconsolately back to Air Force Six-Two-Six to report his failure, Navy Gooney Bird Nine-Two-Three landed, turned around on the runway, and taxied up beside the other aircraft.

Steeling himself for the ordeal, its pilot rose reluctantly from his chair and made his way into the passenger compartment. Admiral J. Kingswood Saltee, who had taken a wee cup of grog to settle his stomach before they had taken off, another wee cup as they lumbered into the sky, and several other cups en route, was sitting in a chair, mouth open, uniform cap somewhat askew, eyes closed and snoring loudly.

The pilot shook his arm. Nothing happened, so he shook it again. The admiral opened his eyes.

'Sir, we're on the ground at Spruce Harbor,' the pilot reported.

'Just resting my eyes a moment,' the admiral said. He examined the empty glass in his hand. 'Put a drop in there, will you, Commander? A little pick-me-up is always in order before inspecting the honour guard.'

'Admiral,' the pilot said, 'about the honours . . .'

'You mean, they're not ready with my honours?' He looked out the window. 'Why, there's nobody out there but a couple of funny-looking civilians. Who are those idiots, anyway?'

'Admiral, I believe that's Senator Cacciatore and Senator Fisch,' the pilot said.

'That's the trouble with national defence,' Admiral Saltee said. 'How can we be expected to do our job with some lousy senator always snooping around finding fault?' He looked out the other window. 'My God, that looks like Air Force three!'

'No, sir,' the pilot said, 'that's Chevaux Petroleum One.'

'Chevaux Petroleum One?'

'Yes, sir. Air Force Three is parked on the other side of it.'

'Tell you what, Commander,' Admiral Saltee said. 'I have decided to dispense with honours. Lieutenant (j.g.) J. P. Jones is somewhere in the area . . .'

'Lieutenant J. P. Jones,' the pilot said, describing what could have been, but what was not, a Grecian urn, with his hand, '*that* Lieutenant Jones?'

'That Lieutenant Jones,' the admiral replied. 'Get in touch with her, and have her lay on a car for me. I'll just take a little nap while I'm waiting.'

'Aye, aye, Admiral,' the commander replied.

Several hours before this happened, Mr. T. Alfred Crumley, administrator of the Spruce Harbor Medical Center, had been informed by Mr. Taylor P. Jambon that Miss Patience Throckbottom Worthington would be checking out and instructed to make arrangements to have her fan mail forwarded to Vienna, Austria.

Mr. Jambon's announcement posed for Mr. Crumley a certain delicate problem. Mr. Jambon had not mentioned Miss Worthington's bill, which by now was rather substantial. It had not occurred to Mr. Crumley to raise the vulgar subject of money on Miss Worthington's admission. One simply does not, Mr. Crumley had decided, raise vulgar subjects to personages such as America's most beloved thespian.

Mr. Crumley believed, as indeed did most of the English-speaking world, that Miss Worthington was sole heir to the tradition and worldly goods of the distinguished acting

114

family of which she was the sole surviving legitimate member. And she was. What the English-speaking world did not know, because it was hard to believe, was that the Worthingtons, to a man (and woman), had spent the vast sums they had earned on the stage, the silver screen and the boob tube as fast (and sometimes far faster) than they had earned them.

Patience Throckbottom Worthington, America's most beloved thespian, didn't have a dime. Not that this sad financial state in any way affected her standard of living. At her father's knee she had learned the secrets of how to live well while without funds. The first secret was never to let it appear that you are either broke or poor. Only the poor, and those who appear poor, have their credit questioned. The rich (and those who are thought to be rich) have unlimited credit; their creditors wish to believe that they will be paid, facts and nasty rumours about the cash values of the customer being grandly ignored.

The second secret was how to deal with those people who control credit. These generally fell into two categories, the tough successful credit-granters (bank presidents and the like) before whom normal people, Category I, were the easiest of all to handle. One simply insulted them, got their names wrong, and spilled drinks in their laps. That quickly tamed them. They simply were unable to believe that someone not in awe of them, someone who treated them with evident scorn and disdain, could possibly have any financial worries.

Category II, those who handled credit for other people (mobile-home salesmen, hotel clerks and hospital administrators, and the like), were accustomed to being abused by their betters and would thus wait patiently through the most virulent tirade, at which point, bloody but unbowed, they would ask, 'Now, about this overdue bill?'

Category II creditors, obviously, had to be treated differently. The Worthington technique over the years had been to treat them with bucketsful of charm, to make them believe that they were far better than was the case and that only one Worthington or another could see the beauty in

115

them. This kept them from bringing up the vulgar subject of money for long periods, but one day, inevitably, the question of the bill would be raised. At this point, after murmuring about nurturing a viper at one's breast, it was only necessary to tell them what you really thought about them and had been thinking all the time.

And so it was when Mr. T. Alfred Crumley presented himself at the foot of the bed of Patience Throckbottom Worthington, in her private room, southern exposure, equipped with theatrical-makeup mirror, refrigerator, portable bar, colour television and some other standard non-hospital items she had gently insisted upon.

'I understand, dear lady,' Mr. Crumley began, 'that you are soon to leave us.'

'Quite so, my dear Mr. Crumley,' Patience had replied, in the soft voice which for thirty years had thrilled millions of Americans as she read Dickens' *A Christmas Carol* on Christmas Eve, first on radio and later on television. Combined with the look she gave him from her gentle blue eyes, it should have been enough to shut him up for a week.

'We shall miss you, Miss Worthington,' Mr. Crumley said. 'Your presence at Spruce Harbor Medical Center has enriched the lives of all who have been privileged in some way to serve you.'

'The show, Mr. Crumley, as I'm sure someone of your deep sensitivity and high intelligence is very much aware, must go on!'

'Your dedication to your art brings tears to my eyes,' T. Alfred replied, dabbing at them with a fresh hankie.

'I am, you know,' she said, deciding to press home the advantage, 'going to Vienna, Austria, there to make a few simple appeals on behalf of America's starving pups and pussies.'

'So I understand, dear lady.'

'Mr. Taylor P. Jambon himself has asked me to make them,' Patience said. 'As ill and in such pain as I am, as you know yourself so well, my dear Mr. Crumley, this will mean a considerable sacrifice on my part. But no sacrifice is too great where darling puppies and sweet pussies are

116

concerned. And who could possibly refuse a tearful entreaty from Mr. Taylor P. Jambon, famous gourmet and animal lover?'

'Who indeed, dear lady?' Mr. Crumley replied.

'A small corner of my heart shall always be reserved for the Spruce Harbor Medical Center and its splendid administrator,' Patience said. 'I shall never forget you, Alfred . . . I may call you Alfred, mayn't I?'

T. Alfred Crumley stopped dabbing at his eyes with his hankie and blew his nose rather loudly into it. With tear-filled eyes, he looked at America's most beloved thespian.

'About your bill, Miss Worthington?' he began.

'Blat!' Miss Worthington said.

T. Alfred Crumley was simply not used to hearing language like that, except, of course, from such crass and low-life personages as the chief of surgery, Dr. Hawkeye, Pierce, and his crony, Trapper John McIntyre. He really couldn't believe his ears.

'Pardon me, dear lady?' he said.

'Something wrong with your bleeping ears, you bleeping four-eyed jackass?' Miss Worthington inquired.

'Miss Worthington!'

'How *dare* you come in here, you bleeping ignoramus, and ask *me* about your miserable bleeping bill?'

T. Alfred Crumley stared at her, open-mouthed.

'Get your blat the bleep out of here, you bleeping creep, before I forget I'm a bleeping lady,' Patience went on.

'But the bill!'

'Bleep you and your bleeping bill,' Patience said, and reaching beside her placed her hand on a certain item of hospital equipment designed to spare patients the necessity of walking barefoot across chilly floors to the inside plumbing.

Her aim, fortunately for Mr. Crumley, was a little off, possibly because she was on her second bottle of Old White Stagg Blended Kentucky Bourbon. The bedpan missed him by six inches before careening off the colour television's cathode-ray tube, which shattered.

The bedpan was followed by the telephone.

'Well!' Mr. Crumley sniffed. 'We'll see about this!'

117

'Out, out!' Miss Worthington screamed, as she tossed one of the Old White Stagg Blended Kentucky Bourbon bottles at him. So piqued was she that she threw the wrong (or quarter-full, rather than empty) bottle.

'Now see what the bleep you made me do!' she screamed. 'Your bill! You have the bleeping nerve to ask me, you blap, about your bleeping bill! I'll tell you what you can do with your bleeping bill!' And she did.

T. Alfred Crumley fled. After spending a few minutes alone in the mop closet to regain his composure, he decided to bring the matter to the attention of the chief of staff. That luminary, so said the Professional Personnel Locator Board, was at the Board of Health. That posed other problems. There was nothing the chief of staff hated more than to be called off the twelfth hole; he grew quite as livid and profane as Miss Worthington. 'Golf, goddamnit,' is as he had said more than once to Mr. Crumley, 'is what it's all about. Can't you see that, Crumley?'

In the absence of the chief of staff, the chief of surgery was the senior ranking medical officer. Mr. Crumley knew that Dr. Pierce was in the establishment. As he had walked by the chief of surgery's office, he had been able to quite clearly hear the blood-curdling sound Alfred the dog made as he playfully gnawed on a three-foot section of oxen thighbone.

Straightening his shoulders and taking a deep breath, he knocked at Hawkeye Pierce's office. The sound of the bone crunching stopped and was replaced by a deep-pitched growl.

'Go away, Crumbum,' Hawkeye called cheerfully from inside. 'You know that you're not one of Alfred's favourite people.'

'Dr. Pierce, I have to see you on a matter of the most pressing importance,' Mr. Crumley called, and after a moment the door opened a crack. Hawkeye sniffed.

'My God, Crumbum, you reek of Old White Stagg!' Hawkeye said. 'Shame on you!'

'That dreadful woman threw a bottle of it at me,' Mr. Crumley said. 'And I'd hate to tell you what else.'

'What dreadful woman?'

'Miss Patience Throckbottom Worthington, that's who!'

118

'America's most beloved thespian? That Patience Throck-bottom Worthington?'

'She's leaving the hospital.'

'Well, then, your problems are over, aren't they?'

'Without paying her bill! When I brought it up, ever so tactfully, she called me a ... I refuse to sully me lips with the language she used.'

'No!'

'Yes!'

'And what precisely is it you wish of me?' Hawkeye asked.

'In the absence of the chief of staff, you are the senior physician in the hospital,' Crumley said.

'Bill collecting is not in my department,' Hawkeye said. 'Sorry, Crumbum.'

'That's Crumley, Doctor,' Mr. Crumley said. 'I keep telling you that, and you just can't seem to remember.'

'On the other hand, Crumbum,' Hawkeye went on, 'maintaining the peace and tranquillity of this place is my business. Getting that broad out of here would certainly have a beneficial effect on the other patients.'

'Not with her bill unpaid!' T. Alfred Crumley protested.

'What about her ardent fan, Taylor P. Jambon?' Hawkeye asked. 'Can we get the money out of him?'

'I hadn't thought of Mr. Jambon,' T. Alfred Crumley confessed. 'I truly hate to bring up something ... distasteful ... like this to America's famed gourmet and animal lover.'

'Which is more distasteful, Crumbum,' Hawkeye asked, 'disturbing Jambon or not getting paid?'

'Thank you, Doctor,' T. Alfred Crumley said. 'I'll return to my office and telephone Mr. Jambon immediately.'

Closing the door on him, Hawkeye thought that would be the end of it. He had returned to his desk and to his monthly correspondence. He had before him a roll of heavy-duty, fibreglass-reinforced plastic tape, a pile of discarded bricks, and a stack of the little cards with which all Americans over the age of six are very familiar, the postage-will-be-paid business-reply coupons with which advertisers tempt the buying public with all sorts of quasi-free offers.

119

'Yes,' read one such postage-paid card, 'I would like to accept your free trial offer of my own barrel stave-making machine, reduced this week to $299.95, with which I may start myself on the path to financial security in my basement.'

Hawkeye had come across the card, and twenty-five more very much like it, firmly stapled into magazines for which he had paid cash money. In order for him to read the stories in which he was interested, it was generally necessary for him to interrupt his concentration, very carefully rip the postage-will-be-paid business-reply coupon from the magazine (unless one ripped very carefully, one generally ripped out the article in which one was interested as well), find a wastebasket for same, and then returned to the magazine. By the time this had all transpired, he had at the very least lost his place, as well as his line of thought, and at worst the magazine had been confiscated by Mrs. Pierce.

Although, as a matter of principle, Hawkeye had as little to do with United States governmental officials as humanly possible, he was so annoyed with the postage-will-be-paid business-reply coupons with which his magazines and mailbox were stuffed that he brought it to the attention of the highest-ranking federal official in Spruce Harbor, Maine, the postmaster.

That official informed him that there was absolutely no law on the books that forbade advertisers ruining magazines with their postage-will-be-paid business-reply coupons or filling his mailbox with direct mail advertising including such postage-will-be-paid coupons.

'When I was a soldier,' Hawkeye said, 'I had a wide reputation as the best guardhouse lawyer north of Chunchon and south of Pyongyang. Lemme see the regulations.'

The regulations were fascinating. They said that while there would be no charge for postage-will-be-paid coupons which were not returned through the mail, the Post Office Department would charge the addressees a small fee, in addition to the regular postage, based on the weight of the item returned, for each such postage-will-be-paid coupon actually used to carry something through the mails.

'Tell me, Howard,' Hawkeye had said to the postmaster, 'what would you do if you got one of these deleted expletive coupons tied to a brick?'

'I'll look into it, Hawkeye, and get back to you,' Postmaster Howard P. Jefferson, who had not risen high in the postal heirarchy by making snap decisions and shooting from the hip, replied.

Two weeks later, after consulting both his superiors and a nephew who was in the second year of law school, Postmaster Jefferson issued his pronuciamento:

'Hawkeye, in reply to your interrogatory of recent date,' he said, 'it is our decision, subject of course to reversal and/or review by higher authority, that if someone, for reasons which escape me, should attach a postage-will-be-paid coupon to a brick or other heavy object, the addressee would be liable for the first-class postage of brick and postage-will-be-paid coupon.'

'You mean he would have to pay first-class postage *by the ounce* for whatever the brick weighed?'

'Theoretically, that is the case,' Postmaster Jefferson said. 'But who would want to do something like that . . . what's in that burlap bag, Hawkeye?'

'Seventeen bricks and seventeen postage-will-be-paid business-reply coupons,' Hawkeye replied. 'Don't let anything stay you from the swift completion of your appointed rounds, Howard.'

Correspondence Day, as Dr. Pierce thought of it, was one of the bright moments of his month. He, personally, was helping reduce the post office deficit. Bricks generally cost the addressee $2.30 in postage each. One particularly dedicated purveyor of phonograph records in Ohio who hadn't learned to take 'no' for an answer was soon going to have enough $2.30 bricks to build a garage.

Since he was, thus, merrily engaged in such a worthwhile practice, it is understandable that Dr. Pierce was a little annoyed when Mr. T. Alfred Crumley, Taylor P. Jambon in tow, reappeared at his office door.

'Now what, Crumbum?' he inquired, not at all kindly.

'Doctor,' Taylor P. Jambon said. 'You have to help me!'

'It is not necessary for you to approach me on your knees, Mr. Jambon,' Hawkeye replied. 'Just telephone my secretary for an appointment, and I will be happy to discuss cutting your throat or whatever else seems to be bothering you.'

CHAPTER TWELVE

Taylor P. Jambon lied well. The story he told Dr. Benjamin Franklin Pierce, chief of surgery of the Spruce Harbor Medical Center was, furthermore, one of his better efforts.

According to Mr. Jambon, Patience Throckbottom Worthington, America's most beloved thespian, was, as the result of her accident, 'in the most severe pain, suffering excruciating agony whenever she had to move. Far too brave to complain, and determined to do what she could to help Americans' suffering pups and pussies,' she had finally resorted to taking 'a glass or two of spirituous liquor' to dull the pain. Being 'wholly unaccustomed to anything stronger than sherry,' and that only once a year, when she had concluded her traditional Christmas Eve rendition of Dickens' *A Christmas Carol*, the sad truth was that she was.

'I say this, Doctor, only because I am sure it will go no further, because of the patient-doctor confidentiality code, a wee bit tipsy.'

'No,' Hawkeye replied, visibly shocked. He had not, of course, believed a word Jambon had so far said. He was curious, however, to see to what heights the Jambon imagination would carry them all.

'Yes,' Taylor P. Jambon said, wiping a tear from his eye.

'I will rush to her side and pump out her stomach,' Hawkeye said.

'No!' Mr. Jambon said, very quickly.

'Followed by a long, cold shower and copious quantities of steaming coffee,' Hawkeye went on. 'After which I will ask Mr. Crumbum here to detect and locate the black-hearted scalawag who has dared to profane the lips of America's sainted thespian-lady with spirituous liquors.'

Taylor P. Jambon looked a little confused.

'If I may continue, Doctor?' Jambon said.

'By all means,' Hawkeye said.

'There is another problem,' Taylor P. Jambon said. 'I'm sure that you are familiar with Senator Christopher Columbus Cacciatore, Doctor?'

'The very sound of his name causes my heart to flutter and my mind's eye to fill with visions of Old Glory fluttering over our nation's Capitol, where that sainted man gives so freely of his time to save us poor taxpayers from our folly,' Hawkeye said.

'Yes,' Jambon said. 'I tell you in absolute confidence, Doctor, that Senator Christopher Columbus Cacciatore, himself, is coming right here to Spruce Harbor, this very afternoon, to take Miss Worthington away.'

'No!'

'Yes!' Mr. Jambon said. 'Senator Cacciatore is one of Miss Worthington's greatest admirers.'

'I can certainly understand that,' Hawkeye said softly.

'And vice-versa,' Taylor P. Jambon said.

'I can understand that, too,' Hawkeye said. 'Birds of a feather, to coin a phrase.'

'Precisely,' Taylor P. Jambon said. Somehow, however, he suspected that things weren't going exactly as he intended them to go. 'Well, Doctor, you can well imagine how absolutely crushed and humiliated our dear Miss Worthington would be if her dear friend Senator Cacciatore should learn that she was, well, a little tiddly.'

'What are you asking of me, Mr. Jambon?'

'I had hoped that a physician and surgeon of your obvious intelligence and vast experience, not to mention compassion, would perhaps be able to think of something that would solve the problem,' Taylor P. Jambon said.

'Tell you what I'm going to do, Jawbone,' Hawkeye said.

'That's *Jambon*, Doctor.'

'Don't interrupt me when I'm displaying my obvious intelligence, vast experience and practically bottomless compassion,' Hawkeye said.

'Sorry,' Taylor P. Jambon said.

'You square the lady's bill with Crumbum here,' Hawkeye said, 'and I'll give her a little something that'll keep her under long enough to get her on the plane.'

'I'm sure,' Taylor P. Jambon said, 'that something can be worked out with regard to her bill.'

'In cash,' Hawkeye said. 'And now.'

'That isn't, exactly, what I had in mind,' Taylor P. Jambon said.

'That is, exactly, what I have in mind,' Hawkeye replied. 'Otherwise, when the senator arrives at our airfield, he's going to find Miss Worthington waiting for him, sitting on her little stretcher, waving her bottle around and singing "Show Me the Way to Go Home"!'

Taylor P. Jambon turned slightly green, but he reached for his wallet.

'And now, Mr. Jambon, if you will excuse us,' Hawkeye said, 'Mr. Crumbum and I will confer privately as to the exact dosage of the depressant I will administer to Miss Worthington.'

'Certainly,' Mr. Jambon said. 'I don't want to know any of the details!'

T. Alfred Crumley, although he said nothing, looked at Dr. Pierce with shock and concern in his eyes. While, it is true, he did not understand at all how someone of Dr. Pierce's general character could possibly be regarded as a first-class chest cutter, he had never believed that he would stoop to administering a drug to anyone without sound medical reason.

As soon as Taylor P. Jambon had left the office, Dr. Pierce went to a filing cabinet, unlocked it and withdrew a gallon bottle filled with a crystal-clear liquid.

'I hope you realize, Crumbum,' he said, 'how this violates my principles.'

'What is that?' Crumley asked.

'Essence de Bayou,' Hawkeye said. 'My very last one.'

'But what *is* it?'

'It is a preparation made with loving care by a first-class craftsman in simpler times,' Hawkeye said. 'It is no longer made. The chemist, so to speak, now can't spare the time

125

from the press of his other duties. The Bayou Perdu still bubbles no more.'

'Are you saying that's ... moonshine? Untaxed, illegal corn liquor?'

'Actually, it's a skilful blend of corn liquor and rice liquor, with just a hint of brandy added to give it a little *je ne sais quoi*,' Hawkeye said. 'It is from the last run, made the day before Chevaux Petroleum bulldozers came to prepare the site for drilling. Horsey gave me six gallons, for auld lang syne, and this, Crumbum, is the last, so to speak, of the last. I tell you this so that you will appreciate what a sacrifice I am personally making in order to get your bill paid and that nasty broad out of our hospital.'

'How much am I supposed to give her?' Crumley asked.

'As much as necessary,' Hawkeye said. 'I should think that a quart would be enough to send even Miss Worthington to dreamland.'

'But is it safe?'

Dr. Pierce looked thoughtful.

'Good thinking, Crumbum,' he said finally. 'It wouldn't do, would it, to give Miss Worthington something we weren't absolutely sure of, would it?' He then bent his mouth over the neck of the bottle, skilfully extracted the cork with his teeth, and with a certain élan, his finger hooked in the bottle ring, threw the bottle over his arm and took a good swallow.

He lowered the bottle, smacked his lips, thumped his chest with his fist, looked thoughtful, and then, finally, smiled.

'Here you go, Crumbum,' he said, handing him the bottle. 'Now get out of here before I change my mind. Noble self-sacrifice, even in a good cause like this one, comes hard to me.'

And so it came to pass, as it says in the Good Book, that as Wrong Way Napolitano's pickup, bearing the secretary of state, Reverend Mother Emeritus, and the chairman and chief executive officer of Chevaux Petroleum International (plus, of course, Darling and Beauregard) rolled somewhat unsmoothly from Spruce Harbor International Airfield towards the Spruce Harbor Medical Center, they encountered, rolling majestically in the opposite direction, the hearse of the Spruce Harbor Funeral Home.

Horsey, Wrong Way and the Secretary of State politely removed their hats as the two vehicles met and Reverend Mother Emeritus raised her hand in blessing.

'She must have just recently gone to the Great Rollcall in the Sky,' Reverend Mother said. 'I saw her husband kneeling beside the corpse. I could even see the tears in his eyes.'

It wasn't, of course, either a corpse or a bereaved husband. It was Patience Throckbottom Worthington being carried to her rendezvous with Senator Christopher Columbus Cacciatore. Taylor P. Jambon, whom Reverend Mother Emeritus had understandably mistaken for the husband, did indeed have watering tear ducts. The tears in his eyes, however, were a physical reaction to the fumes which rose from Miss Worthington with every breath; the look of concern on his face was for his own safety. All it needed was one spark to ignite those fumes, he realized, and they'd be blown up all over the rock-bound coast of Maine.

Taylor P. Jambon, realizing that unless he got some fresh air the hearse would deliver two unconscious bodies to the aircraft, rolled down the window and stuck his head out. His eyes cleared; he saw they were at the airfield. And then he saw something else.

'Stop!' he suddenly shouted. His voice, while not loud, had a certain penetrating quality, like the sound fingernails make when scraping along a slate blackboard. That timbre, plus the fact that the hearse driver wasn't used to receiving orders from the back seat, shocked the driver into action. He took his foot from the accelerator and jammed it on the brakes. The hearse slid to a stop. Patience Throckbottom Worthington, who had been installed on the rolling-wheels arrangement designed for easy removal of a casket, kept moving until she encountered the back of the driver's seat.

It roused her momentarily from her slumber, long enough to deliver a brief, if somewhat scathingly scatological opinion of the driver's skill, intelligence, and obviously canine parentage. Then she resumed, with an awesome snore what was anything but her sleep of innocence.

127

'Jaws,' Taylor P. Jambon said, 'what are you doing wandering around the end of the runway?'

'What are you doing in that hearse, Taylor P.?' Senator Fisch inquired without replying to Mr. Jambon's question. 'Nothing, God forbid, has happened to America's most beloved thespian?'

'Of course not,' Taylor P. Jambon replied.

'Then what are you doing in a hearse?'

'Trying to cheat an honest businessman, that's what he's doing,' the driver said. 'He told me that ugly old broad was a stiff.'

'So I did,' Mr. Jambon said. 'And stiff she is.'

'I meant dead-stiff,' the driver said, 'not drunk-stiff.'

'That's your problem,' Taylor P. Jambon said. 'Get in, Jaws. Which airplane is ours?'

'The medium-sized one,' Senator Fisch said. He stuck his head in the hearse, looked around nervously, and withdrew it. 'You just go ahead, Taylor P.,' he said. 'I'll trot along after you.'

'You're a sissy, Jaws, you know that?' Taylor P. Jambon said disgustedly, slamming the hearse door. 'Drive on,' he ordered.

'I'm not driving two feet until you pay me the live-body rate,' the driver said.

'My good man, do you have any idea who you have the great privilege of ferrying around in your somewhat ratty hearse? Patience Throckbottom Worthington, that's who!'

The driver jumped from behind the wheel. He pulled open the rear door, grabbed Taylor P. Jambon by his shirt-front, and threw him out of the hearse. Then he went to the rear door, opened it, grabbed the stretcher on which Patience Throckbottom Worthington slept soundly, and rolled it out of his hearse. It dropped three feet to the ground, but the bump did not disturb Miss Worthington's sleep.

'I thought that telling me that drunken old broad was dead to get the cheaper stiff rate was the lowest thing I'd ever heard,' the driver said, 'but bringing in the name of Patience Throckbottom Worthington is really rotten. You should be ashamed of yourself!'

'There seems to be a slight misunderstanding,' Senator Fisch said, trying to pour a little oil on the troubled waters.

'And you, too!' the driver said. He slammed both doors, got behind the wheel, slammed the driver's door, and drove off.

'Well, Taylor P.,' Senator Fisch said. 'Now what?'

'Things could be worse,' Taylor P. Jambon said. 'Quick, grab your end of the stretcher.'

'How could they be worse?'

'I could have paid him in advance,' Taylor P. Jambon said. 'If you trot a little, Jaws, and with a little luck, we can have her aboard the plane and be out of here before he remembers I haven't paid him.'

With Miss Patience Throckbottom Worthington suspended between them, they trotted down the runway to Air Force Six-Two-Six. Senator Cacciatore saw them coming. He came down the stairs, took off his pearl-grey homburg and held it over his heart as Senator Fisch and Taylor P. Jambon carried Miss Worthington up the stairs.

'She looks,' the senator said, emotion evident in his voice, 'just as I thought she would.' He dabbed at his eyes with his hankie. 'A saint, that's what she is. A saint! There must be Italian blood in her somewhere.'

He climbed back up the stairs. The stairs folded back into the plane. The engines started. The pilot picked up his microphone.

'Spruce Harbor Departure Control,' he said. 'Air Force VIP Six-Two-Six requests . . .' He remembered where he was. 'Oh, to hell with it,' he said, hanging the microphone up and then shoving the throttle forward. Air Force VIP Six-Two-Six roared down the runway and into the air.

Eight hours later, famous gourmet and animal lover Taylor P. Jambon, accompanied (somewhat reluctantly) by Senator J. Ellwood 'Jaws' Fisch, stole quietly into the airborne bedchamber of Miss Patience Throckbottom Worthington. By custom and tradition, the sleeping compartment of the aircraft was assigned to the senior passenger, military or government official, aboard. In this case, this luminary was clearly Senator Christopher Columbus Cacciatore.

129

Senator Cacciatore had, on learning that Miss Worthington's agony was such that she had to be sedated to bear it, graciously given up his privilege.

'I'm an Italo-American gentleman,' the senator said, 'as well as a United States senator. How could I sleep knowing that sainted lady was suffering out here with the rest of you unimportant slobs?' The senator and Mrs. Cacciatore had passed the flight playing two-handed solitaire.

'Miss Worthington,' Taylor P. Jambon called. 'Patience, dear lady!'

The sainted lady opened one eye, closed it, opened the other one, closed that, and with great effort finally managed the coordination necessary to open both at the same time.

'Who the bleep are you?' she inquired. 'And what the bleep do you want?'

'It is I, Miss Worthington,' Taylor P. Jambon replied. 'Taylor P. Jambon, your most devoted fan.'

'More important, where the bleep am I? And what's that bleeping whistling noise?' Miss Worthington went on.

'We are approaching Vienna,' Taylor P. Jambon said. 'I thought perhaps you might wish to freshen up before we land.'

'The last bleeping thing I remember is pouring a glass of that moonshine,' she said.

'I think you dropped off to dreamland, dear lady, and we saw to it that you got on the airplane.'

'Dreamland, my blat,' she said. 'Somebody slipped me a bleeping Mickey Finn, and then you, you bleep, shanghaied me. I'll have your blat for this, you bleeping degenerate.'

'Vienna, dear lady, is the home of music. Of Strauss, Beethoven, Mozart, Brahms . . .'

'Stick your Strauss . . .' she began.

'. . . and, for the next several weeks,' Taylor P. Jambon plunged on loudly, 'of Boris Alexandrovich Korsky-Rimsakov.'

'Of course,' Patience Throckbottom Worthington said, sounding as she sounded on Christmas Eve before the microphone. 'I had quite forgotten. And how far, you dear man, did you say we were from Vienna?'

130

'About forty minutes, Miss Worthington, Taylor replied. 'We just passed over Paris.'

'Paris with that delightful man would be ever so much better than Vienna,' she said thoughtfully. 'But I suppose one mustn't be greedy.' She turned to Senator Fisch. 'All right, precious,' she said, 'you may set my hair.'

'I beg pardon?' Senator Fisch replied.

'I said, you may set my hair. I must, of course, look my best when I meet dear Boris.'

'What's that got to do with me?' Senator Fisch asked.

'What the bleep do you think it's got to do with you? You're the bleeping hairdresser, aren't you?'

'Madame, I am a United States senator,' Senator Fisch said.

'You're kidding!'

'I am not!' Senator Fisch proclaimed, rather excitedly.

'Jesus, if it waddles like a hairdresser, lisps like a hairdresser, and smells like a hairdresser, it should be a bleeping hairdresser,' Patience said.

'I'll have the stewardess look in on you,' Taylor P. Jambon said. 'And Senator Cacciatore wishes to pay his respects.'

'Look, whatever your name is, one bleeping politician at a time is enough. More than enough,' Patience replied.

'The senator is a devoted fan of yours,' Taylor P. Jambon said. 'I think what he would like to do is ask you to honour him by being his guest while you are in Vienna.'

Patience looked thoughtful. 'I suppose I should have some suitable address of record,' she said. 'There would be talk if I just moved in with dear Boris.' She turned on a smile and switched her tone of voice again. 'Would you please tell the senator I will receive him just as soon as I'm through with my hairdresser?' she said in warm, dulcet tones.

'I told you that I'm not a hairdresser,' Senator Fisch said.

'Take it from me, sweetie,' Patience said, handing him a hairbrush, 'you missed your calling. If anyone ever had a natural talent . . .'

'I will not!' Senator Fisch said, stamping his foot. He looked close to tears.

'Shut up, Jaws,' Taylor P. Jambon said, 'and start brushing!'

CHAPTER THIRTEEN

The next day, in the marble and glass palace of the Amalgamated Broadcasting System in New York City, another hair-brushing took place. To those unfamiliar with the little tricks of the trade, the magic, so to speak, of television broadcasting, it would have looked a little odd. But, since those out there in television land would never be given the opportunity to witness what was going on, no harm was done.

A bald man (not Kojak bald – there was a fringe of mousy looking hair at the level of the ears – but *bald*) sat before a sort of bust, peering at it through thick-lensed glasses, which gave him somewhat the appearance of a guppy. The bust was both lifelike and very familiar. Millions of people would have immediately recognized it as being more than a reasonable (actually an incredible) likeness of America's most handsome young television newscaster, Don Rhotten.*

The bust had the Paul Newman-blue eyes; it smiled, displaying the famous set of pearly white choppers; and it had the familiar Don Rhotten coiffure, dark, thick, luxuriant, and drooping boyishly over the famous Rhotten forehead.

The bust sat on a specially built table, on the rear of which had been erected eight mirrors arranged in a semi-circle so that the head was instantly viewable from eight different angles. From the very latest model loudspeakers (called, in the trade, 'studio monitors') the voice of Don Rhotten filled the room. The famous dulcet tones had been recorded reading *Desiderata*, which the bald-headed man felt presented more of an opportunity to display the full range of Don Rhotten's speaking voice than the somewhat pedestrian-sounding world news he read over the airwaves each night.

As Don Rhotten's voice rolled sonorously on, the bald-headed man mouthed the words (which he knew by heart),

---

*Mr. Rhotten, of Serbo-Croatian ancestry, pronounces his name 'Rowten'.

revealing his own set of choppers, which were mottled yellow, brown and purple and obviously in need of the attention of one of the better corrective dental surgeons.

There was obvious love and boundless admiration in his eyes as he, with infinite tenderness and painstaking care, brushed the thick, luxuriant locks on the bust's head. He used a hairbrush guaranteed to contain nothing but bristles from the chin whiskers of the finest Tasmanian warthogs. The best was none too good where the hair of Don Rhotten was concerned. From time to time, he would raise his eyes to the wall beyond the table. It was covered with 11×14 colour photographs of Don Rhotten, generally close-up shots of his head and shoulders alone, but including a dozen or more photographs of Don Rhotten beaming in mutual admiration at one prominent world figure or another.

Outside the room, mounted above the door, were three red bulbs and a sign reading 'NO ADMISSION WHEN LIGHTS ARE FLASHING.'

Three men came down the marble and plastic-oak-veneered corridors of the building. They paused outside the door when they saw the lights flashing. They were Mr. Seymour G. Schwartz, executive producer of the highest-rated ABS television presention, 'Waldo Maldemer and the Evening News With Don Rhotten'; Mr. Wesley St. James, chairman and executive officer of St. James's Holdings, the Hollywood-based television goliath (some said 'octopus') which included St. James Productions [eight of the more successful daytime dramas (or 'soaps', as they were known in the trade) and St. James Games, which produced nine of the eleven top game shows for example, 'Grovel for Gold' and 'What's My Terminal Illness?']. The third man was as instantly recognizable, as Mr. Rhotten. He was Waldo Maldemer himself, America's most beloved telecaster.

'I could, had you the foresight to seek my counsel,' Waldo Maldemer said in his famous sombre tones, 'have predicted this. The warning lights are illuminated, indicating egress is unwelcome.'

'Shut up, Waldo,' Seymour G. Schwartz said. He tried the door. It was locked from the inside. He knocked even though

133

he realized this would be futile. The door and walls had been heavily insulated to keep the sound of the studio from the dressing room and, equally important, to keep the sound of Don Rhotten's voice, on the tape recorder, endlessly repeating the lines of *Desiderata*, from driving everyone else bananas.

'Kick it down,' Wesley St. James said. He was a slight gentleman, standing approximately five-feet-three in his stocking feet and including about ten inches of what can only be described as a blonde Afro. Like most small men, he was rather belligerent.

'It may be fairly presumed,' Waldo Maldemer said, 'I would not hesitate to suggest, that privacy ranks high among the priorities of the dressing room occupant.'

Seymour G. Schwartz stepped quickly to a large box equipped with a large lever and marked MASTER SWITCH — DO NOT TOUCH! He pulled the switch. For a moment there was total darkness, and then emergency battery-powered lamps came on, giving off a faint light, just enough to see with.

In a moment the door above which, pre-switch throwing, the red lights had flashed burst open and the bald-headed man with the bad teeth and thick spectacles rushed out.

'What the bleep happened to the bleeping lights?' he demanded. Astonishingly he sounded just like America's most handsome young telecaster.

'Don-Baby,' Seymour G. Schwartz said. 'What a coincidence! Waldo, Wesley and I were just going to drop in on you.'

The bald-headed man suddenly rushed back into the dressing room. Wesley St. James tripped him. He flew into the dressing room. The others followed him, closing the door after them. Seymour G. Schwartz bolted it.

The lights came back on.

'I don't know what you guys are up to,' the bald-headed man said.

'Don-Baby!' Seymour G. Schwartz said.

'My dear fellow and esteemed colleague!' Waldo Maldemer said.

'Big Bunny!' Wesley St. James said.

'But whatever it is, you can forget it,' the bald man went on. 'You can only fool Don Rhotten three or four times. I'm wise to you guys!'

'Don-Baby, you don't mean to say you don't trust us?' Seymour G. Schwartz asked.

'That you actually harbour even the faintest suspicion that we have anything but your welfare at heart?' Waldo Maldemer intoned.

'That Little Bunny would do anything to hurt Big Bunny?' Wesley St. James asked.

'You bet your bleeping blat I do,' the bald man said. 'If you guys aren't up to something crooked, my name's not Don Rhotten.'

(A word or parenthetical explanation is obviously required here. Mr. Wesley St. James, Mr. Seymour G. Schwartz and Mr. Don Rhotten had begun their careers in television simultaneously. Mr. Schwartz, as 'Uncle Ralph,' was the undisputed king of Saturday morning kiddie television in Cedar Rapids, Iowa. Decked out in a straw hat, overalls and a plaid shirt, and aided and abetted by Mr. St. James and Mr. Rhotten, who wore rabbit costumes and were known respectively as 'Little Bunny' and 'Big Bunny', he brought mirth, joy, and the latest Chicago hog futures to literally dozens of viewers in the Cedar Rapids area. The world will never know to what heights Mr. Schwartz might have risen as a performer, for fate stepped in and rearranged their lives.

(The television station's anchorman, who delivered the noontime news, dallied a bit too long in the Last Chance Saloon. When he appeared at the studio, he couldn't see the microphone, much less the wire-service copy he was to read. It was decided, in the grand, even sacred, tradition of show biz that the show must go on. The problem there was who could read the news? Uncle Ralph, even without his rubber nose, was obviously too famous a figure to pass himself off as a newsman. Little Bunny was disqualified by a shiner acquired the previous evening in the Last Chance Saloon. That left Big Bunny.

(With something less than unbridled confidence, Seymour

G. Schwartz seated Don Rhotten before the camera, equipped him with a sheet of news-service copy, and ordered the cameraman to focus on him and the engineer to put him on the air. Then he put his hands over his eyes and closed them. Sometimes, he knew, it is really better to do nothing at all, rather than something foolish. And trying to pass Big Bunny off as a newscaster was foolishness of the ultimate degree.

(Amazingly, however, when he couldn't *see* Big Bunny, just hear his voice, a miracle occurred. Don Rhotten's voice oozed warmth, sincerity, wisdom, compassion, understanding and credibility. Mr. Schwartz, frankly, had never listened much to his voice before. All he had previously required of Big Bunny was that he hippity-hop around the stage with his fists tucked under his chin, making bunny noises.

(To cut a long story* short, Mr. Schwartz had the courage to grasp opportunity when it passed his way. First signing Mr. Rhotten to a lifelong contract guaranteeing him seventy-five per cent of all his earnings, he then borrowed sufficient funds from Mr. St. James to equip Big Bunny with a wig, contact lenses, caps for his teeth and his first pair of shoes with laces. He then arranged for a high-ranking television executive to view a film which showed Mr. Rhotten reading news and cutting back and forth between him and other TV biggies such as H. Smith, W. Cronkite, H. Rudd and D. Rather, as they read the news. Big Bunny was better, and everyone could see this.

(The rest is history. Within a matter of weeks, Don Rhotten was a star. Mr. St. James, realizing that there was no place for him in big-time TV news, had bought the controlling interest in an about-to-be-shot-from-the-airwaves soap opera. Brilliantly sensing its weaknesses (the heroine wasn't suffering enough), he did an overnight rewrite, giving the heroine, in addition to her unwanted pregnancy, two

---

*The rise of Messrs. Wesley St. James and Mr. Don Rhotten to the pinnacle of television success is discussed in *M*A*S*H Goes to Las Vegas*, *M*A*S*H Goes to Morocco*, and *M*A*S*H Goes to Hollywood*, all of which may be found at better booksellers' places of business, offered for sale at very reasonable prices.

exotic diseases, an amputated leg, a drinking problem, and an unwarranted indictment for election fraud. Overnight, the soap had soared back to the top of rating lists, and St. James Productions was off and running.

(We left Don Rhotten, you will recall, just after he had said that Mr. Wesley St. James. Mr. Waldo Maldemer and Mr. Seymour G. Schwartz could bet their 'bleeping blats' that he didn't trust them, that he harboured suspicions about their intentions and suspected that they, indeed, wanted to hurt him. We rejoin them now):

'When did we ever fool you, Don?' Wesley St. James said. He walked over to the Don Rhotten bust. 'Say, you really have done wonders with the hair. It *glints* beautifully, gives off little shimmers of health and wholesomeness.'

'You think so, Wesley, or are you just saying that to get on the right side of me?'

'What's this "Wesley" business? You'll always be Big Bunny to me, Don, no matter how great a star you've become, no matter how simply smashing your hair looks. And *boy*, does it look *good*! Howard K. Smith, eat your heart out!'

'I am sort of happy with it,' Don Rhotten said, somewhat shyly. 'It's my own idea, Little Bunny.'

'Your own idea, Big Bunny? Well! I don't suppose you'd care to tell me what you put on it?'

'I wouldn't tell anybody but you, Little Bunny,' Don Rhotten said.

'I appreciate that, Big Bunny,' Wesley St. James said solemnly.

'Mazola,' Don Rhotten said.

'Wow!' Wesley St. James said. 'It really takes a Don Rhotten to think that out for himself, doesn't it, fellows?'

'I mean,' Don Rhotten said, 'grease is grease, you know? I mean, I can get a whole gallon of Mazola for a couple of bucks, and I'm paying like seven-fifty for two lousy ounces of Parisian Hair Pomade.'

'I always said ol' Big Bunny had a head for figures,' Wesley said. 'Wasn't I saying that just before we came here, fellas?'

137

'You sure were, Wes,' Seymour G. Schwartz agreed.

'I remember it quite clearly,' Waldo Maldemer said.

'I was thinking, Seymour,' Don Rhotten said. 'If I gave it a little plug on the show, you know, let people know that I use Mazola on my hair, do you think the Mazola people would slip me a couple of gallons for free?'

Seymour G. Schwartz winced.

'Don't take offence, Don-Baby,' Seymour G. Schwartz said, 'but don't you think that for a great big star, an international star, of television newscasting, such as yourself, that trying to mooch a couple of lousy gallons of corn oil is a little, well, *déclassé*?'

Don Rhotten looked thoughtful. 'Seymour,' he said, 'you know I don't speak Russian.'

'That's Polish, I believe,' Waldo Maldemer said. 'Either Polish or Swedish.'

'What he's saying, Big Bunny,' Wesley St. James said, 'is that you would look like a piker.'

'Seymour, you can't talk to me that way!' Don Rhotten said. 'I'm Don Rhotten, you know.'

'Tell you what,' Wesley St. James said. 'I'll send you a case of mazola, Don, O.K.? Gallon cans.'

'Make sure it's polyunsaturated, whatever the hell that means,' Don Rhotten said.

'I will,' Wesley St. James said. 'But I was listening to what Seymour said, Don, and he had a point.'

'What kind of a point?' Don Rhotten asked suspiciously.

'He said that for "a great big international star", such as yourself. You heard him say that, Waldo, didn't you?'

'I heard him say that, Wesley,' Waldo Maldemer agreed.

'So I'm a great big star,' Don Rhotten said. 'I know that. So what?'

'The key word is "*international*" star, Don,' Wesley said.

'What's that supposed to mean?' Don Rhotten replied, his eyes narrowing.

'It's an adjective, Don,' Waldo Maldemer offered. 'Existing, constituted, or carried on between nations . . .'

'Shut up, Waldo,' Seymour G. Schwartz said.

'I think I know what you dirty bloppers are up to,' Don Rhotten said. 'And the answer is "no".'

'I don't have any idea what you mean, Big Bunny,' Little Bunny said. 'Do you know what Don is talking about, Waldo?'

'I would say, Wesley, that he has surmised our purpose in coming here,' Waldo Maldemer replied.

'Shut up, Waldo,' Seymour G. Schwartz said.

'If you guys came here to talk me into leaving New York,' Don Rhotten said, rising to his full height of five feet, six-and-one-half inches, 'you got another think coming.'

'Don-Baby,' Wesley St. James said, 'think about it. How are you going to be an *international* television newscaster if you never leave New York?'

'I'll fake it,' Don Rhotten replied immediately. 'The way the other guys do. Rear projection. The engineers can work it out.'

'That's not the same thing as the real thing, Don,' Seymour G. Schwartz said.

'You know it isn't,' Don Rhotten said. 'Bleep the real thing.'

'What have you got against a little trip, Don?' Wesley St. James said.

'You know bleeping well what I've got against it,' Don Rhotten said. 'You know what happens every time I get out of New York.'

'I forget,' Wesley St. James said. 'Tell me, Big Bunny.'

'O.K. Seymour told me I had to go to Israel. So what happened? I got sand under my rug, that's what happened.'

'He's right,' Waldo Maldemer said. 'I remember the incident vividly.'

'Shut up, Waldo,' Seymour G. Schwartz said.

'And then I went to Morocco. They put me in jail in Morocco.'

'And what happened in jail?' Wesley St. James said. 'What *nice* thing happened in jail, Don? 'Fess up.'

'O.K.,' Don Rhotten said, 'so I met Smiling Jack in jail.'

'Your best friend, right? If you hadn't gone to jail, you wouldn't have met Smiling Jack, right?'

139

'Congressman Jackson* to you, Wesley,' Don Rhotten said. 'Show a little respect.'

'No disrespect intended, Big Bunny,' Wesley St. James said, immediately and with fervour. 'You know that. But the bottom line, Big Bunny, is that if you and that beloved solon had not been in the Casablanca slammer together, you never would have become pals, right?'

'O.K. But so what?'

'So you really came out of the slammer smelling like a rose, right, Big Bunny?'

'I did not!'

'Figuratively speaking, of course,' Wesley St. James said. 'And, Big Bunny, now that you've had a little time to think it over, you really had a good time in Maine, didn't you?'

'You're crazy, Little Bunny, that's what you are!' Don Rhotten replied. 'If you think my idea of having a good time is getting thrown in the Maine State Penitentiary with Waldo Maldemer.'

'Come on, Big Bunny,' Wesley St. James said. 'Didn't the governor himself tell you he was sorry about the little misunderstanding? And give you a lobster, just to show there were no hard feelings?'

'And that bleeping lobster bit me on the nose!' Waldo Maldemer said.

'He was just trying to be friendly, Waldo,' Seymour G. Schwartz said. 'He let go, didn't he?'

'He had to be pulled off,' Waldo said. 'And you know it!'

'I'm not going anywhere, Little Bunny,' Don Rhotten said with conviction and absolute determination.

*Mr. Rhotten here referred to the Honourable Edwards L. Jackson (Farmer-Free Silver, Ark.), third ranking member of the House Committee on Sidewalks, Subways and Sewers. Although, in the interests of national security, neither the House of Representatives nor the State Department are willing to discuss the matter at all, it has been reliably reported that Congressman Jackson was detained by the Moroccan authorities in Casablanca, apparently because both the Moroccan authorities and the U.S. consul in Casablanca believed he was an escapee from a mental institution.

'Whatever you say, Don-Baby,' Seymour G. Schwartz said. 'We'll change the subject. What do you think of Taylor P. Jambon?'

'A genius,' Don Rhotten replied immediately, 'A man who understands the sacrifices we television journalists make in the pursuit of our careers. Isn't that right, Waldo?'

'Absolutely,' Waldo Maldemer. 'One of the most astute minds of the age.'

'Taylor P. Jambon said that you and Waldo were the *crème de la crème* of television newscasters, didn't he?'

'Well,' Don Rhotten said, 'it's true, isn't it? Why shouldn't he say it?'

'Absolutely,' Seymour G. Schwartz said. 'And what about Senator Cacciatore?'

'Who's he?'

'Senator Christopher Columbus Cacciatore,' Wesley St. James said.

'Give me a little hint,' Don said.

Wesley St. James began to sing: 'Santa Lu-chee-ah!' he sang. 'Santa Lu-chee-ah!'

'Oh,' Don Rhotten said. 'That one. The Jewish fella.'

'Italian, Don,' Wesley St. James said. 'But you were close.'

'The one who holds hearings on television every year and find fault with everything, right?' Don Rhotten said. 'Now I remember. He's got a red nose.'

'That's the one,' Wesley said. 'What would you say, Don, if I were to tell you that Senator Cacciatore and Taylor P. Jambon are friends?'

'I don't believe it.'

'Tell him about Miss Worthington, Wesley,' Seymour G. Schwartz said.

'You remember Miss Worthington, Don, of course?' Little Bunny said. 'Miss Patience Throckbottom Worthington?'

'The one who always reads Dickens' *A Christmas Carol* on Christmas Eve?' Don Rhotten asked.

'Right the first time, Don-Baby,' Seymour G. Schwartz said. 'Like I was saying to Wesley, Don-Baby's really into culture. Wasn't I saying that, Wesley?'

141

'I don't remember that,' Waldo Maldemer said.

'Shut up, Waldo,' Seymour G. Schwartz said.

'What about Miss Worthington?' Don Rhotten asked.

'Miss Worthington, Taylor P. Jambon and another great American, Senator J. Ellwood Fisch . . .'

'I know him,' Don Rhotten said. 'He's the one with the teeth!'

'Right,' Wesley St. James said.

'The one who bit the broad in L.A.,' Don said. 'I saw the wire-service copy.'

'Wash your mouth out, Big Bunny,' Wesley St. James said indignantly. 'You're talking about *my* senator.'

'I tell you, Little Bunny, I saw the copy. He bit her on her upper thigh.'

'Look at it this way, Don-Baby,' Seymour G. Schwartz said. 'If she was a good girl, what was she doing with her leg in the senator's mouth?'

'The whole thing was blown out of proportion. It was nothing more than a friendly little nibble anyway,' Wesley St. James said.

'Well, what about him?' Don Rhotten asked.

'Tell me, Don,' Seymour G. Schwartz asked, 'what do you know about APPLE?'

'There's red ones and yellow ones,' Don said thoughtfully. 'And little sour ones.'

'Not that kind of apple, dummy,' Wesley St. James said. 'APPLE. The Association of Pup and Pussy Lovers in Earnest.'

'Huh?' Don Rhotten replied.

'That's what APPLE means,' Seymour explained.

'Oh, sure. That's what Mr. Jambon is always pitching,' Don Rhotten said, 'with that clever, clever jingle: "Send us a Dollar a Day, and We'll Keep the Dog-catcher Away." He's really a good man, that Taylor P. Jambon.'

'Taylor P. Jambon needs your help, Wesley St. James said solemnly.

'Television stars aren't supposed to *give* money to worthy causes,' Don Rhotten replied. 'We ask *other* people to give. I thought you knew that, Little Bunny.'

'I'm not talking about money,' Wesley St. James said.

'A plug on the show? That's up to Seymour, Little Bunny. How much are they offering?'

'This is a special kind of plug, Don-Baby,' Seymour said. 'One that only you can do.'

'And I will hold things down when you're away,' Waldo Maldemer said, 'and give the good people out there in television land day-by-day reports of your travels.'

'You're a little early with that, Waldo,' Seymour said.

'What do you mean, while I'm away?' Don Rhotten asked.

Little Bunny, humming *Tales from the Vienna Woods*, began to waltz around the room.

'Say, you're pretty good at that,' Don Rhotten said. 'But don't try to change the subject. What did Baggy Jowls here mean about my "travels" and "when I'm away"?'

'We're going to Vienna, Don,' Seymour G. Schwartz said. 'Little Bunny and me.'

'Bring me back a Wiener schnitzel,' Don Rhotten said.

'And we want you to come with us.'

'Bleep you,' Don Rhotten said. 'I ain't going.'

'Here's the bottom line, Don-Baby,' Seymour G. Schwartz said. 'Mr. Taylor P. Jambon and Miss Patience Throckbottom Worthington are in Vienna to shoot some public-service commercials for APPLE.'

'What's that got to do with me?'

'Senator Cacciatore and Senator Fisch are with them,' Seymour went on. 'And we have worked out sort of a little arrangement, Don.'

'Have fun,' Don Rhotten said. 'Now, if you will excuse me, it's time I got ready for my broadcast.' He reached into a drawer and came out with a small plastic box. From it, he took what looked like a set of false teeth. He slipped these over his own choppers and examined himself, with obvious satisfaction, in the mirror.

'Nothing written down, of course,' Seymour went on, 'but Senator Cacciatore has sort of agreed that if we make him look good in Vienna, he'll lay off us with the blood-violence-mayhem business in this year's hearings.'

'Nobody pays attention to him anyhow,' Don Rhotten

said. 'So what's the difference?' He was now bent somewhat awkwardly over the table with the mirrors, and the casual observer would have thought he was sticking his thumbs in his eyes. The cognoscenti, however, those privileged to know the secrets of TV magic, knew that what he was really doing was inserting his Paul Newman-blue contact lenses. When they were finally in place, he examined himself in the mirror and winked at his own image.

'I'm getting a little something out of this, too,' Wesley St. James said. 'You want to help Little Bunny when he's in trouble, don't you, Big Bunny?'

'Not if it means leaving town,' Don Rhotten said. 'What kind of trouble?' he reached over and took the wig from the bust and carefully arranged it on his head. 'You'd think,' he said, as he always said on this occasion, 'that a country that can put a man on the moon would be able to come up with a rug glue that really worked, wouldn't you?'

'They're working on it, Don-Baby,' Seymour G. Schwartz said. 'But think of Wesley's problem. You know how much money he spent promoting the new soap . . .'

'That's daytime drama, Seymour. Try to remember that,' Little Bunny said.

'The new daytime drama,' Seymour said. 'And then what happened?'

'Miss Patience Throckbottom Worthington had her tragic accident, that's what happened,' Little Bunny said. 'All that dough down the drain with her in a hospital bed, her leg in a cast.'

'I keep getting back to this,' Don Rhotten said, and with his wig, caps and contacts in place, he looked like the famous face which beamed nightly from the tube. He looked, in other words, confident, assured, competent and trustworthy. The transformation was spectacular. 'What's in it for me?'

'A quick flight to Vienna,' Seymour began.

'Absolutely no!'

'Where you do a couple of little human-interest features, as straight news.'

'Let Hanging Jowls go,' Don Rhotten said. 'I'll hold things down for him while *he's* away and give the folks out there in television land a daily report on *his* travels. The bottom line of the features, Don,' Wesley St. James said, 'is that *my* star, Patience Throckbottom Worthington, is such a saint that she rose from her bed of pain to make public-service commercials for APPLE before coming back to my show.'

'She really did that?' Don Rhotten asked.

'I'd hate to tell you what it cost,' Seymour G. Schwartz said and then quickly recovered, adding, 'that saintly woman in terms of excruciating agony to make this sacrifice on behalf of the nation's starving pups and pussycats.'

'That's really touching,' Don Rhotten said, dabbing at his eyes.

'And we tie her in with Cacciatore and Fisch,' Seymour said. 'That gets Cacciatore off our back and sort of discredits the foul rumours circulated by his unscrupulous political enemies that Fisch gets his jollies biting hookers.'

'I still don't see why Hanging Jowls can't do it,' Don Rhotten said.

'Two reasons,' Little Bunny said.

'Say,' Waldo Maldemer said, 'he called me "Hanging Jowls" again. He promised not to do that.'

'It slipped out,' Little Bunny said. 'No offence intended, right, Big Bunny?'

'Why can't he?' Don Rhotten pursued.

'It's right there in our contract,' Waldo Maldemer went on. ' "Mr. Rhotten agrees that he will cease and desist referring to Mr. Maldemer as 'Jowls', 'Hanging Jowls', 'Sagging Cheeks', 'El Chipmunk', and from any and all other derogatory and/or insulting references to Mr. Maldemer's . . ." '

'Shut up, Waldo,' Seymour G. Schwartz said.

'. . . facial conformation,' Waldo concluded righteously.

'Don-Baby,' Seymour G. Schwartz said, 'we thought about sending Waldo.'

'I didn't know that.' Waldo said.

'Shut up, Waldo,' Wesley St. James said.

'But finally concluded this was your kind of story.'

'Why?' Don Rhotten asked, his tone dripping with cynicism.

'Because it calls for someone with an all-around image of

youth,' Wesley St. James said. 'And besides, Miss Worthington asked for you. She's one of your greatest fans.'

'Miss Patience Worthington is one of *my* fans?' Don Rhotten asked, beaming. 'Oh, you're just saying that!'

'Am I not, either,' Wesley St. James said. 'Am I, Seymour?'

'She said that, Don,' Seymour said. 'She said, "I just love Don Rhotten".'

'Well, why didn't you say so?' Don Rhotten said. 'I will, of course, be happy to do what I can.'

'We knew we could count on you, Don,' Wesley St. James said. 'You're booked on the seven-thirty flight to Vienna tomorrow morning.'

CHAPTER FOURTEEN

While things didn't really turn out, at least at first, as bad as Lieutenant (j.g.) J. P. Jones, U.S.N., feared they would, her duties in Spruce Harbor could not really be described as being without certain problems.

She had, of course, anticipated that Woody's sponsors would give a little 'welcome home' party for him, since he had confided to her at Annapolis that he really felt a familiar relationship to Drs. Pierce and McIntyre and their families.

In her mind, even after she had been made privy to Woody's noble lineage, she had seen a happy little family group, in paper hats, gathered around a family dining room table, blowing little horns and singing 'Happy Birthday, Dear Woody, Happy Birthday to You.'

What she got was the First Annual Welcome Home Woody Banquet and Clam Bake at the Bide-a-While Pool Hall/Ladies Served Fresh Lobster & Clams Daily Restaurant and Saloon, Inc., presided over by His Honour Mayor Moosenose Bartlett of Spruce Harbor and featuring music by the Spruce Harbor High School Marching Band. It was vacation time at Spruce Harbor High, too, of course, and the only musicians in town happened to be the bass drummer, two tuba players and the glockenspiel virtuoso.

While their rendition of 'God Save the Queen' was perfectly satisfactory, their version of 'The Star-Spangled Banner' was frankly a disaster, and when they proceeded from that (via 'Anchors Aweigh') to music for dancing ('Red Sails in the Sunset' and, for reasons Lieutenant (j.g.) Jones could not fathom, 'Stars Fell on Alabama'), things grew worse.

None of this discouraged the enthusiastic dancers. Woody and Beverly danced slowly and closely together, and it was quite evident that for all they cared the band could have been

147

playing the Triumphal March from *Aida*. Doctors Pierce and McIntyre performed an odd ritual with their mates that both healers apparently believed to be the fox trot.

Mayor Moosenose Bartlett periodically rose to his feet to deliver a somewhat incomprehensible political oration, ceasing only when someone poured a pitcher of beer over his head, at which point all two-hundred guests would applaud enthusiastically.

The notion that there are women who are perfectly prepared, and happy, to go through life without a male at their side had apparently not reached Spruce Harbor, Maine. Lieutenant (j.g.) Jones was introduced seven times to a 'nice young man', 'just the fella for you', 'somebody with really good prospects', and so on, who in every instance turned out to be Richard Wilson, M.D.

The banquet lasted until two in the morning. At six-fifteen the same morning, Lieutenant (j.g.) Jones wakened from a mildly disturbing nightmare (in which it was Dr. Wilson, rather than Alfred the dog, taking undue familiarities with her person) by what sounded like a diesel truck's air horn outside her window.

What it was was a diesel truck air horn mounted upon the oddest-looking vehicle she had ever seen. It had four tyres, each eight feet tall and two feet wide. In it were Woody and Beverly and Dr. Wilson.

'We're going clamming in the swamp buggy,' Woody called up to her. 'It's jolly good fun!'

As a person, she could not deny him his 'jolly good fun', and as a naval officer it was clearly her duty to accompany him. She had been warned, of course, that she could expect to make, in the course of her naval career, many personal sacrifices. But in her wildest dreams, she had not considered that these sacrifices would entail mucking around on the Spruce Harbor mud flats rooting out clams, up to her knees and elbows in black goop, while an enormous dog and a male chauvinist looked down at her from a swamp buggy, their eyes full of unabashed love.

For the first time since he had arrived in Spruce Harbor, Alfred the dog had not gone with Hawkeye to the hospital. It

148

quickly became apparent that Alfred the dog had joined her party and had every intention of staying until the party was over, no matter how long that took. For the first few days, Lieutenant (j.g.) Jones had regarded Alfred the dog as simply one more barb in her crown of thorns, but then she realized that there was a definite advantage in having a large Scottish wolfhound extremely fond of you.

Particularly if one also had a large medical person simultaneously, and quite as shamelessly, enamoured of one. Alfred the dog became immediately jealous of the attention being paid to Lieutenant (j.g.) Jones by Richard J. Wilson, M.D. Whenever the doctor ever so casually laid his arm on the back of the seat on which he sat with Lieutenant (j.g.) Jones, Alfred the dog pushed it away with his paw. Whenever Dr. Wilson turned his face towards Lieutenant (j.g.) Jones, with osculation clearly in mind, his pursed lips touched not Lieutenant (j.g.) Jones's delicate white skin but Alfred the dog's large, cold black nose.

As Alfred the dog sank in Dr. Wilson's estimation, he rose in Lieutenant (j.g.) Jones's. She had no time for romance. She was a naval officer, her life dedicated to the briny deep, and while she realized that eventually a gentleman might come into her life, he would be a knight in navy white, not an amiable apprentice chest-cutter in surgical green.

It wasn't that she didn't like Dr. Wilson. She thought he was sweet. But she didn't want a *sweet* boyfriend. She wanted a boyfriend with machismo, a boyfriend who would sweep her off her feet, not touch soft fingers to her brow and tell her it was time to get out of the sun, she was a little feverish.

On the other hand, she had convinced herself that if that sacred naval custom provided each sailor with a girl in each port, in the new, revised scheme of things that now meant that each sail-person was entitled to a romance-person of his or her choice in every port.

Dr. Wilson had been selected for that singular honour. She knew she would think of him fondly as the years passed, on lonely nights on the bridge of the aircraft carrier she would one day command, that sweet little doctor with the blue eyes and warm hands back in Spruce Harbor, Maine, with whom she had once shared a too brief, bittersweet moment of passion.

To accomplish this end, she chose a clamming costume consisting of not quite enough material to make a decent-sized handkerchief. What there was of it, however, was liberally soaked in 'Free Ms.,' new perfume absolutely guaranteed to drive male chauvinist sexists mad. Then, taking into account the fact that the only thing Alfred the dog liked better than guarding her virtue was eating, she hid aboard the swamp buggy a bag of dog food (the large, kennel-sized bag) and three gallons of water with which to mix it in the cut-off bottom of a fifty-five-gallon drum Alfred the dog used as his puppy bowl.

When they reached the mud flats she sent Woody and Beverly off alone, to slop about happily hand-in-hand in the mud.

'Dr. Wilson and I will watch you from the buggy,' she said.

As soon as they were gone, she turned to Dr. Wilson and Alfred the dog, both of whom seemed to be sitting on their haunches, wagging their tails, lolling their tongues, and staring at her with undisguised adoration.

'Dick,' she said, 'I think Alfred is hungry.'

'He's not hungry,' Dr. Wilson replied. 'While we were waiting for you and Beverly to come out of the nurses' quarters, he stole two hams from the hospital kitchen.'

'He looks hungry to me,' she insisted.

'Too much food isn't good for a dog,' Dr. Wilson said.

'Do me a favour and feed the damned dog, will you?' she said.

'Whatever you say,' Dr. Wilson said. 'All I ask from life is the opportunity to make you happy, even if that will probably make the dog throw up.'

He climbed down off the swamp buggy. She handed him the bottom of the fifty-five gallon drum, and then the bag of dog food, and finally the three plastic gallon bottles of water. While he was stirring the mixture, she removed the terrycloth robe she had been so far using to cover the 'Free Ms.'-soaked bikini and arranged herself seductively on the rear seat of the swamp buggy.

She felt Dick's weight as he started to climb back up the ladder. Suddenly embarrassed, she turned to look out at the mud flats and the harbour itself. Suddenly, her heart beat faster, and she knew that it was now or never, for sailing majestically up the harbour, the national colours waving in the breeze, was the nuclear submarine USS *Satyriasis*.

Dr. Wilson, in navy parlance, 'reached the top of the ladder'. He looked at Lieutenant (j.g.) Jones. While, in his line of work, he was not entirely unfamiliar with large expanses of naked female flesh, none of it before had ever produced the reaction in him that this did. His heart started to beat with a strange rapidity. His head felt light. More importantly, the palms of his hands began to sweat.

'Oh, Joanne!' he cried. She turned to look at him shyly, just before his sweaty palms slipped off the rungs of the ladder and he fell off the ladder. Horrified, Lieutenant (j.g.) Jones heard the sound of his body crashing onto the ground. She jumped off the seat, ran to the edge of the swamp buggy and looked down. Dr. Wilson was lying, unconscious, on the ground. Lieutenant (j.g.) Jones went down the ladder after him and bent over his inert form.

'My darling,' she cried, 'what have I done to you?'

Alfred the dog, hearing the 'Oh, Joanne!', the sickening thud, and the 'Oh darling' business came at a run. Since his beloved sail-person was kissing the unconscious body, that was obviously the thing for him to do, too. Wagging his tail, he licked Dr. Wilson's unconscious face.

Lieutenant (j.g.) Jones, after first tenderly kissing Dr. Wilson's somewhat sweaty forehead, remembered that she was a naval officer and could not panic in a time of disaster. She scurried back up the ladder into the swamp buggy, started the engine, and began sounding the buggy's horn in the traditional short-short-short-long-long-long/short-short-short of the SOS.

Far away on the mud flats, she saw Woody and Beverly look in her direction and then start towards her at a run (or at least as much of a run as they could make through the mud). Lieutenant (j.g.) Jones then went quickly back down the ladder to Dr. Wilson.

He stirred.

'Darling,' she said, 'you're alive!'

'I seem to have suffered a simple fracture of either the radius or the ulna,' Dr. Wilson said matter of factly. He sat up then, amazed. '*What did you call me?*'

'Nothing,' she said, flushing mightily. She looked away in abject embarrassment. She saw the USS *Satyriasis*, had steamed even further up the harbour. Her deck (if the exterior portion of her body can properly be called a deck) and stabilization wings, jutting out from the side of the conning tower, were lined with sailors.

'Yes, you did, too!' Dr. Wilson said. 'You said it twice, once when you first came down and again just now.'

She looked at him and met his eyes. He put his arms out to embrace her. Since one of them, as he had professionally noted, contained a fractured radius or ulna, there was a certain degree of pain. He passed out.

'Oh, my darling!' Lieutenant (j.g.) Jones said again, throwing herself on him, holding him in her arms.

'Pardon me, miss,' a firm masculine voice said. 'If you are the party responsible for issuing the SOS, I am Lieutenant Commander Cooper Morton of the United States Navy at your service.'

Torn between two sacred demands on her attention, Lieutenant (j.g.) Jones chose duty. She got off her knees, straightened and saluted.

'Lieutenant (j.g.) Jones, J. P., sir,' she said. 'There has been an accident!'

'I recognize you now, Lieutenant,' Lieutenant Commander Cooper Morton said. 'Who's the civilian?'

'He is Dr. Wilson,' Lieutenant (j.g.) Jones said, 'and I think I've killed him!'

'Got fresh, did he?' Commander Morton said, 'Gave him a regulation karate chop, huh?'

'Sir, your accusations are unfounded.'

Woody came running up.

'I say, what have we here?'

He bent over Dr. Wilson. Beverly Chambers came up, somewhat impolitely pushed him out of the way and put her head on his chest.

'He said he had a fractured radius,' Lieutenant (j.g.) Jones said, 'whatever that is.'

'He's broken his arm,' Woody said. 'I once broke my radius. That's how I came to Spruce Harbor in the first place, as a matter of fact.'

'Who's the Limey?' Lieutenant Commander Morton asked.

'Sir,' Woody said, coming to attention, 'Midshipman Woodburn-Haverstraw.'

'His Grace the Duke of Folkestone,' Lieutenant (j.g.) Jones added.

'Yes, *sir!*' Commander Morton said.

'There's a first-aid kit in the buggy,' Beverly Chambers said. 'Somebody get it. We'll immobilize his arm and take him to Spruce Harbor Medical Center.'

Woody headed up the ladder.

'Get on the radio,' Beverly Chambers said, 'and tell the hospital we're coming.'

Getting on radios was obviously the sort of thing a naval officer was expected to do. Commander Cooper Morton started up the ladder to the buggy after Woody. Alfred the dog, of course, had no way of knowing that Commander Morton was trying to help. It looked to him as if the man was chasing Woody. Alfred the dog didn't think it was nice for people to chase Woody. He put his paws on the side on the buggy and took Commander Morton's leg in his mouth. He didn't bite his leg, or even grip it very hard. He just held him there. Commander Morton, who had seen the movie *Jaws*, looked down to see what was holding his leg and lost his cool. He started to clamber desperately upward. What he grabbed, however, instead of the ladder rung he was reaching for, was Woody's leg.

Woody came tumbling back down, landing on top of Commander Morton. Alfred the dog started to lick his face. Commander Morton lay just as still as he possibly could.

'Are you all right, Woody?' Beverly asked, turning from her attentions to Dr. Wilson.

'Nothing serious,' Midshipman His Grace the Duke of Folkestone replied. 'But if you are going to call the hospital, you'd better make it two broken radii.' He winced and then went on. 'Or is it radiuses? Alfred, let the nice man up. He has to use the radio.'

The USS *Satyriasis* sailed with the tide the next morning, carrying aboard her eleven foreign national midshipmen, including Midshipman His Grace the Duke of Folkestone, whose right arm was in a cast, and their escort officer, Lieutenant (j.g.) Joanne Pauline Jones, U.S.N.

The Honourable Secretary of State, looking just slightly hung over, made a little speech. The blessings of the diety upon the voyage were invoked by the Reverend Mother Emeritus Margaret H. W. Wilson, and the Spruce Harbor High School Band played both the national anthem and 'Anchors, Aweigh!'

The latter musical selection, played as the USS *Satyriasis* actually backed from the pier, was disturbed by several happenings not on the official programme of events. Alfred the dog, seeing the people he loved next best to Hawkeye Pierce, Lieutenant (j.g.) Jones and midshipman Woodburn-Haverstraw, sailing away, began to cry. He was joined in this lament by his adopted uncle, Wee Black Doggie, and by his sisters and brother, Duchess, Darling and Beauregard. The mournful sound of the howling of near-grown Scottish wolf-hounds to which was added the basso tremolo of one full-grown animal, so disturbed the engineman of USS *Satyriasis* that he confused his captain's orders, and went FULL AHEAD on the port engine and FULL ASTERN on the starboard engine, instead of the other way around, and a collision between the USS *Satyriasis* and the Spruce Harbor municipal garbage barge, *The Pride of Maine*, which had been decked out for the occasion in suitable patriotic bunting, resulted.

No lasting damage was done, and as Mayor Moosenose Bartlett, a passenger on *The Pride of Maine* at the time, later said, in years to come the good citizens of Spruce Harbor could point with pride to *The Pride of Maine* as the only garbage barge proudly bearing marks of an encounter with a nuclear submarine.

Admiral Saltee, however, saw only that the prestige of the U.S. Navy had been sullied twice in two days. (The first time, of course, being when Lieutenant (j.g.) Jones, charged with the simple task of getting the Duke of Folkestone aboard the *Satyriasis* in one piece, had miserably failed. He didn't want to hear the details. The bottom line was that a VIP in custody of the U.S. Navy had wound up with a busted arm.)

He ran to the end of the dock, shouting, 'I want that engineman's name!' He had time to shout this twice before he found himself sailing through the air to end up with a large splash in the waters of Spruce Harbor itself.

'I didn't see dat,' the Secretary of State said to Dr. Pierce. 'I didn't see a thing. I vas looking in duh udder direction entirely. If ennybudy vas to ask me, did I see you shove duh admiral off the dock, I don't know from nudding.'

'Come along, Tubby,' Hawkeye said. 'Trapper and I want a word with you.'

'Vatch it vit dat "Tubby" business, will you please? I mean, tink about duh prestige uf duh United States government.'

'Tubby, looking at your smiling face, your jiggling jowls and pearly whites, so to speak, on the tube, you'd never guess what a hard-nosed, cold-blooded, insensitive character you really are.'

'You're insulting me again,' the secretary said. 'You doing it to keep in practice, Hawkeye, or maybe there's a purpose?'

'You mean to tell me you didn't see the unmitigated sorrow on the dock?'

'You mean, did I hear dem dogs howl? How could I miss it?'

'I refer to His Grace the Duke of Folkestone,' Trapper said.

'He *personally* assured me, wise guy, on his word as an English gentleman, dat the arm don't hurt much. Just a liddle.'

155

'I thought the whole purpose of this operation was to keep His Grace happy,' Trapper asked.

'You mean he's not happy? I mean, vat else can ve do? Ve gif him a ride on a nuclear submarine. Dat don't make him happy?'

'You didn't see the tears in his eyes, his stiff upper lip?'

'To tell you the the truth, I didn't notice,' the secretary confessed. 'You want to tell me vat's bothering him?'

'You didn't see the looks he was exchanging with Beverly? It was enough to melt even your heart, Tubby.'

'Frankly, I vas watching the udder guy. I never saw a doctor crying before.'

'We, too, are human,' Hawkeye said. 'Foul rumours to the contrary.'

'He's really god it bad for dat lady sailor, don't he?' the secretary said.

'You're standing in the way of true love,' Trapper said. 'Twice.'

'Dat's duh vay duh ball bounces,' the secretary said.

'What if His Grace realizes that you're the reason that he's two-hundred feet under the Atlantic, going further away from his lady love with every turn of the screw?' Hawkeye asked.

'You vant to run dat by again? What's vit duh screw?'

'Those things on the bottom of the ship,' Trapper explained. 'That turn around and around?'

'So dat's vhat dey call dem!'

'What if His Grace decides that the way to get back at the guy who keeps separating him from his lady love is to rent his seaport to somebody else?'

'He vouldn't do dat!' the Secretary of State said. 'He's an Englisher gentleman.'

'Not unless someone put a few well-chosen words in his ear, he wouldn't,' Trapper said.

'Who vould do something rotten like dat?' the secretary protested, considering the matter, and added. 'Either one of you two vould, come to think of it. O.K. So vat do you vant from me?'

'I thought you would never ask,' Hawkeye said.

156

'Before you slip it to me, I god to tell you the USS *Satyriasis* ain't going to turn around and come back.'

'That thought had crossed my mind,' Trapper said.

'I can't tell you vy, but it ain't going to stop more than a couple of minutes in Herstead-on-Heath, just time enough to let them get off.'

'Then where's it going?'

'I can't tell you, of course,' the Secretary of State said. 'The Russians shouldn't know. But if you vas to ask me was it going to the Mediterranean, I vouldn't lie to you.'

Admiral Saltee at this time rejoined the party.

'Mr. Secretary!' he said, rushing up, shaking a two-pound Croaker out of his left pants leg. 'You're all right, thank God!'

'Vy shouldn't I be all right? You know maybe something I don't know?'

'There's assassins afoot!' Admiral Saltee said. 'Some dastardly foreign agent pushed me into the harbour.'

'No!' Hawkeye said.

'Tell me, Admiral,' Trapper said. 'How much trouble would it be to get Lieutenant Jones and Midshipman Woodburn-Haverstraw off the USS *Satyriasis*?'

'You mean now? While it is proceeding across the broad Atlantic, on a secret course at a classified flank speed, at a depth beneath the surface which would make the Russian Navy eat its heart out, if they found out how deep, which they won't?'

'Right,' Trapper John said.

'Virtually impossible.'

'That hard, huh?' Trapper John said.

'It would entail,' Admiral Saltee said, frankly a little pleased that he was going to have a chance to show off his vast nautical knowledge, 'first of all, authority from the highest, and I mean the *highest*, headquarters. Possibly even as high as a deputy assistant under-secretary of the navy. I mean, really *up* there!'

'And what else?' Trapper said. The Secretary of State mopped his sweaty brow.

'For reasons I cannot divulge, especially to a lousy civilian

157

such as yourself, Doctor, the navy just doesn't park its submarines on the surface in the middle of the Atlantic Ocean, where any Ivan, Dmitri, or Sergei can get a good look at them.'

'I don't follow you,' Trapper John confessed.

'In order to take somebody *off* the *Satyriasis*, Doctor,' the admiral said, somewhat haughtily, 'you'd have to have something to put them *on*. Right?'

'He's got you there, Trapper,' Hawkeye said. 'Go on, Admiral.'

'And what that means is that there would have to be a rendezvous.'

'I see what you mean,' Hawkeye said.

'With a ship just as fast as the *Satyriasis*, so that they could run alongside each other and effect the transfer by breeches buoy.'

'That's that rope thing they hang a people-basket on?' Trapper asked.

'Correct,' Admiral Saltee said. 'Which means that the rendezvous ship would have to be as fast as the *Satyriasis*.'

'Tell me, Admiral,' Hawkeye said. 'Why would it have to be a ship? I mean, why couldn't the *Satyriasis* just pop up on top of the water long enough for a helicopter to pick people off?'

The admiral looked stricken.

'Impossible,' he said.

'Why?'

'It's never been done before. Of *course*,' he added, 'the aircraft fleet aboard the *Enterprise* includes a passenger-carrier which is capable of carrying anybody anywhere.' He paused and took a deep breath. 'We wouldn't want the Kremlin to know, of course.'

'Of course not,' Trapper John said.

'My, isn't this interesting?' Hawkeye said. 'A pay phone in its own booth right here on the pier. What won't Ma Bell think of next?' He stepped inside, deposited a dime, dialled the operator, and handed the phone to the Secretary of State. 'If Whatsisname is slaloming down the hills, try the other guy in the bank,' he said.

Thirty-five minutes later, a radiogram flashed out from the Pentagon.

OPERATIONAL IMMEDIATE

TO COMMANDING OFFICERS
USS SATYRIASIS
USS ENTERPRISE
AT SEA

USS SATYRIASIS AND USS ENTERPRISE WILL CHANGE COURSE AND PROCEED AT FLANK SPEED TO THE NEAREST SPOT AT WHICH A HELICOPTER TRANSFER OF THE FOLLOWING OFFICERS FROM SATYRIASIS TO ENTERPRISE MAY BE EFFECTED.
JONES, LIEUT JG JOANNE PAULINE, USN
WOODBURN-HAVERSTRAW, MIDSHIPMAN, ROYAL NAVY (TEMPORARY DUTY USN)
ONCE TRANSFER TO ENTERPRISE HAS BEEN EFFECTED, ENTERPRISE WILL TRANSPORT NAMED OFFICERS BY PASSENGER CARRYING AIRCRAFT TO VIENNA, AUSTRIA. FOR YOUR INFORMATION, THIS OPERATION HAS BEEN ORDERED BY THE PRESIDENT AND COMMANDER IN CHIEF AT THE REQUEST OF THE SECRETARY OF STATE, WHO HAS INFORMED THE PRESIDENT AND COMMANDER IN CHIEF THAT HE WILL EXPLAIN LATER. CONSEQUENTLY, PLEASE DON'T ASK QUESTIONS, JUST DO IT.

FOR THE COMMANDER IN CHIEF
THE CHIEF OF NAVAL OPERATIONS

CHAPTER FIFTEEN

A small intimate 'Welcome to Vienna' supper was to be given in the Drei Hussaren Restaurant, just off Kärntnerstrasse, in Vienna's inner city, by His Excellency Franz Schubert von und zu Gurkelhausen, deputy chief of protocol for the Austrian government.

His Excellency Johannes Brahms von und zu Uberderbrücke, chief of protocol for the Austrian government, who had originally been scheduled to host the little supper, had been at the last minute assigned by His Excellency the Foreign Minister to attend to the needs of two visiting American politicians, and Franzl (Little Franz as he was known to his intimates) was, so to speak, thrust into the breach.

Frankly, he was delighted. While he felt just a little sorry for his boss, getting stuck with a couple of American politicians, that was the way the schnitzel bounced. The bottom line was that *he* was to have the great pleasure and distinguished honour of hosting, on behalf of the Austrian government, not only the world's greatest opera singer, Boris Alexandrovich Korsky-Rimsakov, but also certain members of the Maestro's intimate entourage, who were, understandably, the *crème de la crème* of international society.

There had been, since what His Excellency referred to as the temporary restructuring of things,* precious little opportunity to do things properly. He had spent most of his diplomatic career catering to the pedestrian whims of one trade delegation or another, or showing stumble-footed travel agents around the baroque palaces, castles and hunting lodges, in order that they would encourage uncouth hordes of tourists to visit quaint Austria, bringing with them thick folders of traveller's cheques.

---

*He referred to the dissolution of the Austro-Hungarian Empire at the end of World War I. Like most Austrians, especially bureaucrats and members of what had been the nobility, he expected to wake up one morning soon to find the king-emperor back on the throne and things back to normal.

Franzl had nothing against hordes of free-spending tourists. It was just that he preferred the other Vienna, the Vienna of gentlemen in tails, ladies in floor-length dresses, with champagne flowing and the silver and crystal glimmering in the flickering light of a thousand candles, whilst violins throbbed hauntingly in the background.

The tourists, and the trade delegates, in His Excellency's experience, preferred to stand around Vienna's famed, historic Ring (the broad avenue which circles the inner city) with a frankfurter* in one hand and a bottle of beer in the other, whistling at the girls.

Tonight was going to be different. Tonight it was going to be wine and roses.

There had first been a priority intergovernmental memorandum from the Ministry of Culture. In Austria the Ministry of Culture is an important facet of government, not at all like its American counterpart, the President's Council on the Arts, which ranks somewhere below the American Committee for Honesty in Government in influence.

The Minister of Culture had informed the Minister of Foreign Affairs that long, hard work of his staff had succeeded in accomplishing what the Foreign Ministry had failed to do: Boris Alexandrovich Korsky-Rimsakov had agreed to forgive the Austrians for what he considered to be a slanderous review of his last performance published in the *Wiener Kourier* (*Vienna Courier* – the most important newspaper). He would sing again at the Vienna State Opera.

The Minister of Culture wished to inform the Minister of Foreign Affairs that he had every confidence his colleagues would see to it that the Maestro was received with appropriate honours and suitable fanfare, and that, so long as he chose to honour Vienna with his presence, the Foreign Ministry would see that the Maestro's path would be, if not

*The familiar American delicacy known as the hot dog was actually invented in Europe, almost simultaneously in Frankfurt, Germany, and Vienna. A hot dog served in Vienna is known as a frankfurter; the same thing served in Frankfurt is known as a wiener. *Wien* being the odd way the Viennese insist on spelling Vienna.

strewn with roses, then at least swept clean of the smallest pebble against which 'Lieber Boris' might stub his toe.

The Minister of Culture's interest in the happiness of Boris Alexandrovich Korsky-Rimsakov was mingled admiration for his art and enlightened self-interest. In addition to having a set of pipes that were truly extraordinary, Maestro Boris Alexandrovich Korsky-Rimsakov was, in the quaint American phrase, boffo at the box office.

All it took, any place in the world, was the slightest rumour that Boris was going to sing, and the box office of the local opera house was quite literally besieged by opera lovers (ninety per cent of them female) fighting for the privilege of buying a seat, with price no object.

So popular was the singer with members of the gentle sex that certain extra expenses were incurred whenever he performed. These included the "Korsky-Rimsakov Curtain", a stoutly constructed device (cyclone fencing reinforced with steel bars) erected from the well of the orchestra pit to the top of the proscenium arch and designed to protect the singer (and other members of the cast) from the hail of heavy hotel keys, bouquets of flowers and items of intimate feminine apparel with which his fans bombarded him whenever he paused for breath. It also served to discourage his fans from leaping onto the stage. The best they could do was throw themselves at the curtain. It was easier to pluck them from the curtain like dead moths than it had been to chase them around the stage.

It was also necessary to reinforce the security personnel, on the order of three-to-one, to protect the singer from his fans and his fans from each other. Other measures were also necessary.

These extra expenses so disturbed the general manager of the French National Opera in Paris that he had, five years before, announced that a surcharge would be necessary for any performance of the man the French referred to as 'Cher Boris'. A twenty-five per cent increase in the price produced not a complaint, and the French, who have a feeling for matters of this nature, upped it to fifty per cent. When this, too, was accepted without a murmur from any of Cher Boris' devoted female legions, it was increased to seventy-five per cent, and then, finally, a new category of performances ('Performances Magnifique') became part of French Opera tradition. A 'Performance Magnifique' differed from a run-of-the-mill Performance Ordinaire only in that it included *Cher* Boris in the cast, and tickets cost exactly twice as much.

It was shortly after the first season of Performances Magnifique that Mr. Korsky-Rimsakov was declared by the president of the Republic, with the advice and consent (indeed, the cheering) of the Chamber of Deputies, a national treasure of the French Republic.

The other major opera houses (Berlin, the Metropolitan, La Scala, Covent Garden, and, of course, Vienna) were quick to copy the Paris innovation of Performances Magnifique whenever *Cher* Boris could be prevailed upon to perform. But the singer seldom left Paris.

'I don't know what it is,' he once confided to a reporter from the *Opera News* (a publication of the Metropolitan Opera Guild), 'the broads, or the booze or the chow, but there's a certainly *je ne sais quoi* about Paris that makes me hate to leave.'

The singer was originally scheduled to arrive from Paris by air, at Schwechat Airfield, but a last-minute cable had announced that he would, instead, arrive by train.

'*Ach, du lieber Gott!*'* said the Minister of Culture to His Excellency Franz Schubert von und zu Gurkelhausen. 'What if he has a sore throat?'

'Look for the silver lining, Excellency,' Franzl replied. 'If he comes by train, he'll arrive at the West Bahnhof. All those crazy women will be at Schwechat.'

'Not crazy women, Franzl,' the Minister of Culture said. 'They're *music lovers*. Try to keep that in mind.'

'*Jawohl*, Herr Minister.' Franzl said.

And find out why he changed his mind and came by train,' the minister said.

Franzl got on the telephone and telephoned the Austrian Embassy in Paris. They didn't have the information readily

* Roughly, 'Oh, my goodness!'

163

at hand but promised to find out just as soon as they could and send it by telegram. The telegram arrived forty-five minutes before the train.

TO HIS EXCELLENCY FRANZ SCHUBERT VON UND ZU GURKELHAUSEN
DEPUTY CHIEF OF PROTOCOL
FOREIGN MINISTRY
VIENNA

IT HAS BEEN ESTABLISHED BY CONTACT WITH THE ROYAL HUSSID EMBASSY HERE THAT MAESTRO BORIS ALEXANDROVICH KORSKY-RIMSAKOV WILL TRAVEL BY TRAIN BECAUSE HIS PARTY INCLUDES THE DOWAGER DUCHESS OF FOLKESTONE, WHO DISLIKES AEROPLANES, AND HER CONSORT, MR. ANGUS MACKENZIE, V.C. FOR FURTHER INFORMATION, THE SINGER WILL BE ACCOMPANIED BY HIS ROYAL HIGHNESS CROWN PRINCE, HASSAN AD KAYAM, AMBASSADOR EXTRAORDINARY AND PLENIPOTENTIARY TO THE REPUBLIC OF FRANCE AND TO THE COURT OF ST. JAMES'S. IN ADDITION, THE PARTY INCLUDES THE BARONESS D'IBERVILLE AND ESMERALDA HOFFENBURG, THE BALLERINA. THEY ARE TRAVELLING ABOARD THE PRIVATE RAILWAY CAR OF THE PRINCE OF LUXEMBOURG.

MAX SCHULTZ
CHARGÉ D'AFFAIRES

His Excellency Franz Schubert von und zu Gurkelhausen was ecstatic. It was going to be like the old days, private royal railway cars, a baroness, a dowager duchess, and a royal highness.

He made a hurried call to the Drei Hussaren restaurant, telling them to shine up some extra candelabra and hire three more violin players. He then commandeered the last remaining limousines* at the local rent-a-car to carry the extra, unexpected, but most welcome noble guests.

* The word limousine is relative. The cars commandeered were, in fact, repainted Ford sedans which had seen previous service as staff cars of the United States Army in Germany.

And then he put on his stiff collar, his morning coat, his striped pants and his silk top hat and was driven to the West Bahnhof. The band was already in place, warming up. The red carpet had already been unrolled.

And finally, around a bend, the train appeared. Franzl's eyes watered. He hadn't ever seen before a train with the flags of royalty snapping from the locomotive except in the movies.

There hadn't been time, of course, to learn the official national anthem of the kingdom of Hussid,* much less to rehearse the band in its performance, so Franzl, in his official role, was forced to make a snap decision.

'Play "The Sheikh of Araby",' he ordered.

'*Jawohl*, Excellency,' the bandmaster said and turned to his ensemble. 'And uh one, and ah two . . .' he began, raising his baton.

The train slid smoothly into the station. And kept sliding. Instead of stopping where Franzl and the red carpet and marching band stood, it slid another hundred yards down the platform, shooting off clouds of steam.

Then with Franzl in the lead, the welcoming party marched, at double time, down towards where the train had actually stopped. Franzl saw that the train had arrived somewhat sooner than the Maestro himself had anticipated. The Maestro, attired in a silk dressing gown, was on the observation car, a chicken leg in one hand, a bottle of champagne in the other. As Franzl watched, he shared the champagne, without benefit of glass, with a rather ruddy-faced gentleman wearing what Franzl thought at first was a skirt but quickly recognized to be a Scottish kilt.

The band suddenly stopped playing, literally in mid-beat. Franzl looked over his shoulder and saw that they were running in the opposite direction. He looked at the train. Sixteen flamboyantly robed Arabs, each clutching a sub-

---

*This was probably a good thing. 'Guggle-Gotoil', the Hussidian national anthem, is a monotone composition scored for two one-string guitars and the jawbone of an ass which instruments were not in the hands of the Vienna Police Force Trumpet, Tuba, Xylophone and Bass Drum Marching Band.

machine gun, had jumped from the stairs of the car preceding the royal Wagon-Lits and taken up defensive position.

Franzl, who understood that royal personages travel with a bodyguard, was terribly embarrassed. Then he was terribly confused, for as he watched, the bodyguard scattered towards the station itself, in visible terror.

Then a motherly appearing woman descended from the stairs of the royal car. She had dog leashes in her hand, and Franzl logically concluded that she was a lady-in-waiting to Her Grace the Dowager Duchess of Folkestone. Dowager duchesses, in Franzl's experience, had a rather universal (and somewhat revolting) habit of possessing small lapdogs, over whom they gushed and cooed until it was necessary to attend to certain natural functions, whereupon the little animals were turned over to some helpless underling for what was euphemistically referred to as 'a walk'.

As Franzl watched, the motherly lady got a good grip on the leash and gave a mighty heave. Franzl paled. What appeared to be a medium-sized, if somewhat skinny, black bear came down the steps, followed by what bore an extraordinary resemblance to a photograph he had once seen of a black Bengal tiger.

The band meanwhile had gathered its courage and members (save one tuba player, who had climbed a lamp pole and was stuck there) together again and resumed the welcoming concert.

According to protocol, to which science Franzl had devoted many hours of study, the national anthem of the senior visiting dignitary was played first, followed in turn by the national anthems of the others, in order of their rank. The dowager duchess of Folkestone was the second ranking personage aboard the train. The band began to play 'God Save the Queen'.

The words, as everyone knows, go, 'God save our gracious queen, Long may she reign supreme,' and so on.

Suddenly, in the instantly recognizable voice of Boris Alexandrovich Korsky-Rimsakov, singing along, so to speak, at full volume came the words:

'My country, 'tis of thee, sweet land of liberty!'

The motherly looking lady-in-waiting stiffened. Franzl was prepared for the to-be-expected British reaction to what, after all, was a parody of their national anthem. But what he expected was, at most, a typical British snort of disgust at the behaviour of the barbaric Americans. What he got was a voice, slightly higher pitched, but every bit as loud as that of the Maestro.

'Boris,' the lady bellowed, 'Knock that off! I told you I don't think you're funny!'

Boris stopped in midsentence. There was a pause.

'Sorry, Florabelle!' he shouted from the observation platform. 'I got carried away!'

The lady-in-waiting taking the animals, whatever they were, for a walk was obviously named Florabelle.

'Frau* Florabelle,' Franzl said, bowing deeply. 'Perhaps you would be good enough to tell Her Grace that I am here.'

'What did you call me?' she asked.

'A thousand pardons,' Franzl said. This old biddy was a long way the far side of fifty, but if she wanted to insist on publicly proclaiming her unmarried status, far be it from Franz Schubert von und zu Gurkelhausen to call her anything but what she wanted. '*Gnädies†* Fräulein Florabelle . . .'

'Why, young man, why do you persist in calling me by my first name?'

'What would you prefer that I call you?' Franzl said, a trifle roguishly.

'Try "Your Grace" on for size, Dutch,' the dowager duchess said.

'A *hundred* thousand pardons, Your Grace,' Franzl said. 'I kiss your hand.'

The dowager duchess extended her hand. The black Bengal tiger on the leash did something that convinced Franzl that whatever it was, it wasn't a tiger. It barked at

* The term *Frau* is applied to married women and to women over a certain age whether or not they have landed a man. *Fräulein* is applied to young, unmarried women. There is no German equivalent for Ms.
†*Gnädige* (adjective) means 'gracious'. As a rough rule of thumb, it is applied to the better-looking *Frauen* and *Fräuleins*, or to any female which appears to be annoyed and/or about to lose her temper.

him. It wasn't very much of a bark, but it was unmistakably a bark and not a meow.

'Fascinating animal,' Franzl said.

'We are all quite fond of Wee Baby Brother,' the dowager duchess said. 'He thinks he's a dog, don't you know?'

'Indeed?'

'What did you say your name is?' the dowager duchess asked.

'A million pardons, Your Grace,' Franzl said. 'I am Franz Schubert von und zu Gurkelhausen, deputy chief of protocol for the Foreign Office. I am here to welcome you officially to Vienna.'

'How do you do?' the dowager duchess said.

And what is that?' Franzl asked, pointing at Wee Black Runt.

'That's Wee Black Runt,' the dowager duchess explained. 'He thinks Wee Baby Brother is his baby brother.'

'I see,' Franzl said. 'Of course.'

'And they are both looking forward so very much to seeing the rest of the family. Do you happen to know, Mr. . . . whatever it was you said . . . whether Horsey is here yet?'

'I beg pardon, Your Grace?'

'Horsey telephoned to say that he, Hot Lips, Hawkeye and Trapper John were flying in. Do you know if they have arrived?'

The British, Franzl knew, more precisely the upper-class British, had the odd habit of addressing one another by strange nicknames. It was thus quite understandable that His Excellency mistook Her Grace's comment. What she meant to say was that Wee Black Runt and Wee Baby Brother anticipated a reunion with their brothers and sisters, Duchess, Beauregard, Wolfie-Baby, Darling, and Alfred the dog. Plus, of course, the uncle, Wee Black Doggie. *That* family. Franzl got the idea that the dowager duchess was referring to her family. Indeed, whom but the most intimate members of her family would a dowager duchess refer to as 'Horsey', 'Hot Lips', 'Hawkeye' and 'Trapper John'?

'I don't believe so, Your Grace,' Franzl said. 'But rest assured. They shall be welcomed in a manner befitting their

168

station, or my name is not Franz Schubert von und zu Gurkelhausen.'

'How sweet of you!' the dowager duchess said. 'And is the duke here?'

'I don't believe so, Your Grace,' Franzl said. 'I feel sure that I would have been told had His Grace arrived.' He paused and bit the bullet. 'Your Grace, might I presume to inquire when *Unser Lieber Boris* might be leaving the train.'

'I don't really know,' the dowager duchess said. 'He's quite health conscious, you know, and at breakfast he said that he was going to have to exercise. The Baroness d'Iberville and Miss Hoffenburg ... the ballerina, don't you know ... said they would exercise with him. Afterwards, dear Boris always likes his little nap.'

'I see,' Franzl said. 'Well, that will give me a minute or two to arrange for the arrival of the duke and the others.'

'Stop that!' the duchess said.

'I beg your pardon?' Franzl asked.

'I wasn't speaking to you,' she said. 'I was speaking to Wee Baby Brother. I sometimes wish he knew he was a cat, so he could take care of that sort of thing in a proper kitty-litter box.'

Franz Schubert von und zu Gurkelhausen followed Her Grace's eyes. The conductor of the Vienna Police Force Trumpet, Tuba, Xylophone and Bass Drum Marching Band, his baton raised high, was looking down with mixed disbelief and horror. Wee Baby Brother, who had acquired his habits from his canine stepbrothers, was, his left rear leg cocked high, accomplishing, against the bandmaster's gold-striped trousers, that act which is accomplished by the male of the species standing up.

'Wee Baby Brother,' the duchess said, 'you are a bad, bad boy!'

Wee Baby Brother began to bark, not well, it is true, but bark and happily. Franzl turned to see what he was barking at. Boris Alexandrovich Korsky-Rimsakov was descending from the Wagon-Lits car.

'Silence, you schizophrenic feline,' he said. Wee Baby Brother sat down and wagged his tail from side to side.

'Welcome to Vienna, Maestro!' Franzl said.

'Who are you?'

'Franz Schubert von und zu Gurkelhausen,' Franzl said, clicking his heels together and making a little bow. 'I am here on behalf of the Foreign Ministry.'

'Tell me, Fritz,' Boris said, 'where is he?'

'Where is who, Maestro?'

'The great healer, the divine psychiatrist, that sage who has unlocked man's mind.'

'I'm afraid, Maestro,' Franzl replied, 'that he is dead.'

'Dead? What happened to him?' Boris looked stricken.

'I believe it was the complications of old age, Maestro.'

'Old age? He's only forty-five years old. And when I talked to him on the phone yesterday, he was in the best of health.'

'You talked to Sigmund Freud on the telephone yesterday, Maestro?'

'I refer, you simpleton, to the sainted sage of Manhattan, Kansas, Dr. Theosophilus Mullins Yancey.'

'I've never heard of him,' Franzl confessed.

'Hassan!' Boris said. His Royal Highness appeared almost immediately.

'Yes, Maestro?'

'I thought you assured me, you overweight camel jockey, that Dr. Yancey would be taken care of. This character says he never heard of him.'

'The doctor awaits you in your hotel, Maestro,' Hassan said.

'Take me to the Hotel Sacher then, and quickly.'

'There has been a slight change of plans, Maestro,' Hassan said. 'With everybody coming, the Sacher couldn't take care of all of us.'

'So what did you do?'

'I rented the Bristol Hotel, Maestro. All except one floor, which is being used by some American politicians. Senators, I believe.'

'God, the minute I turn my back, you throw me together with scoundrels . . .' Boris began. He stopped suddenly and gestured towards the station. 'My God, here they come!'

170

he went on. 'I hold you,' he said, jabbing his finger at Franzl, 'personally responsible for my safety!'

Down the platform, at a dead run, came an unruly mob of at least two hundred women, of, as they say, all degrees and positions of life. Some were in the first blush of womanhood; others were as old as the dowager duchess. But they all bore looks of rapture realized on their faces as they saw their idol.

And even as Boris spoke, the first hotel key came soaring through the air to clatter at Boris' feet.

The choice of the Vienna Police Force Trumpet, Tuba, Xylophone, and Bass Drum Marching Band to perform at the station had been anything but coincidental. The possibility that something like this would happen had been carefully planned for. The bandmaster dropped his baton, blew three times on his whistle, and took a hard hat from his music bag. The other musicians abandoned their instruments, grabbed nightsticks and formed a flying wedge around the singer.

'We have an armoured car right over this way, Maestro,' the bandleader said.

'Just a minute! Just a minute!' Boris said. He looked around him. 'There he is! Wee Baby Brother! Come along, you paranoid pussycat!' he said. Wee Baby Brother ran after him. When they reached the armoured car, Wee Baby Brother jumped on top. Boris jumped inside. Franz Schubert von und zu Gurkelhausen jumped in after him and slammed the door.

'You're safe now, Maestro,' he said. 'They can't get at you in here. We'll have you safe and sound at the Bristol Hotel in no time at all.'

'You know, Fritz,' Boris said, thoughtfully, 'for a moment there, I was afraid I had been away so long that I had been forgotten.'

'How could anyone forget you, Maestro?' Franzl said.

'How indeed?' Boris replied. 'Wasn't that foolish of me?'

The armoured car moved off. Wee Baby Brother stood on the roof barking at all the crazy ladies who ran after it.

CHAPTER SIXTEEN

Despite the anguished protests of the American ambassador (who knew that hell hath no fury like a senator scorned), the management of the Bristol Hotel refused to rent either the Imperial Suite, or the Royal Suite, or even the Bridal Suite to the United States government to house the official U.S. Senate Ad Hoc Committee to Investigate the Mistreatment of Kangaroos and Other Innocent Beasts.

The entire hotel, the ambassador was informed, had been reserved by the Hussidian ambassador to the Republic of France and the Court of St. James's, who was in town for the Performance Magnifique at the opera, and it was only through the graciousness of His Royal Highness that the politicians and their entourage were getting any rooms at all.

'His Royal Highness,' the managing director sniffed, 'for reasons which quite escape me, is friendly towards you Americans, and when I explained the situation to him, he said that I might let you Americans have rooms he doesn't need, providing you agree to using the rear entrance, the service elevator, and to stay out of sight as much as possible.'

The ambassador's instructions, from the State Department's Bureau of Senatorial Relations, had been explicit. Senator Christopher Columbus Cacciatore and his party wished to be accommodated in the 'first-class hotel nearest the opera'. What proximity to the opera had to do with mistreated kangaroos was not quite clear to the ambassador, but his, he knew, was not to reason why, but solely to get out there and keep the senators happy.

Two first-class hotels are close to the opera, the Sacher and the Bristol. When he approached the Sacher about senatorial accommodations, they laughed at him. The Sacher had lost far too many valued American guests when the word had leaked out that politicians were in the house; they wanted no more.

The Bristol, which sits on the corner of the Ring across

Kärntnerstrasse from the State Opera, was his only choice. Rising to the challenge, the ambassador had a large sign hastily painted, reading 'OFFICIAL SENATORIAL ENTRANCE,' which, when erected, neatly covered the sign reading 'SERVICE AND EMPLOYEE ENTRANCE.'

On his arrival, Senator Cacciatore had been pleased with the senatorial entrance. The ambassador was then free to see about tickets for the opera. That was going to be an even greater problem. Performances Magnifique were scheduled, and tickets for those were as hard to find (he was a little shamed at the metaphor which came to mind) as honest politicians.

Senator J. Ellwood 'Jaws' Fisch (Moralist-Liberal, Calif.) looked out the window of his suite of the Bristol Hotel with fascination. His suite was located in the rear of the building, and its windows opened on the alley behind the hotel, the rear entrance of the opera, and the front door of the Hotel Sacher.

There was a good deal of activity in front of the Hotel Sacher. Police barricades had been erected, and fifty of Vienna's finest were waging a barely successful war against approximately three-hundred-fifty females of various descriptions, who (although Senator Fisch did not, of course, know this) were attempting to get inside where they believed, erroneously, Boris Alexandrovich Korsky-Rimsakov was resting his beautiful head.

Senator Fisch was fascinated. While most of the ladies were a bit past their prime, here and there amongst them were younger beauties. Certainly, the senator reasoned, the odds were that among them would be at least one or two, or perhaps three or four, who would be impressed with the machismo of a United States senator.

As he watched the flashing limbs, as the ladies literally tried to crawl over one another, the solemn vow the senator had taken after the unfortunate nibbling incident in L.A. of absolute marital fidelity henceforth and forevermore, vanished instantly.

He was just about to leave the room for a breath of fresh air, and perhaps a bite to eat, when something else caught his eye.

Something else had appeared on the street, something which caused the distinguished solon to open his mouth even wider than it normally hung.

'Taylor P.,' he called, 'you wouldn't believe what I just saw out there.'

'Just cool it, Jaws,' Taylor P. Jambon said. The famous gourmet and animal lover was in the rest facility of their suite, washing a bunch of grapes in an item of plumbing that seemed to be designed for just that purpose. There was sort of a little shelf inside, and when you turned the water on, it sprayed upward, bathing the grapes.

'Come look,' the senator repeated. 'I wouldn't believe it if I didn't see it with my own eyes.'

'You start biting these Austrian broads, Jaws,' Taylor P. Jambon said, 'and Senator Cacciatore hears about it, you'll blow the whole bit.'

Mr. Jambon, however, picked up his bunch of grapes from the grape-washer and walked to the window. He was, after all, he told himself, a connoisseur of all things, including the female of the species, and whatever else one could (and did) say about the senator from California, he did have an eye for the broads.

'Look at that, Taylor,' Senator Fisch said, 'on top of the armoured car.'

'What the hell is it?'

'It's a black Bengal tiger, that's what it is,' the senator replied. 'It must be some kind of a circus.'

'Don't be ridiculous, Jaws,' Taylor P. Jambon replied. 'What would a circus be doing backing up the official U.S. Senatorial Entrance to this hotel? It must be some other member of the Senate Ad Hoc Committee, freeloading.'

'Well, look for yourself,' Jaws replied. 'That's just what they're doing.'

Then he shrieked.

'My God!' Taylor P. Jambon said.

What has caused the senator to scream and the animal lover to exclaim was what had happened. The armoured car's rear door had opened. A squad of policemen had jumped out, ready to do battle. A very large man had then run quickly

174

from the armoured car into the hotel. Then the black Bengal tiger had made a flying leap off the roof of the armoured car into the hotel. It was clear to both men that the beast was attacking whoever had just entered the hotel.

'The poor man!' Senator Fisch said. 'He'll be torn in tiny pieces and eaten alive.'

'We can only hope he is a Republican,' Taylor P. Jambon said. 'Did you recognize him?'

'He moved too quickly,' Jaws said. he started for the door.

'Where are you going?' Taylor P. Jambon said.

'There will be television cameras,' the senator said. 'I want to be among the first to express my profound shock at the tragic loss to our country of the distinguished senator whoever that was.'

'You have a point,' Taylor P. Jambon said. 'With a little luck, I can get on camera and say the only reason that tiger ate him is because he was starving.'

Carrying his bunch of grapes in his hand, Taylor P. Jambon followed Senator Fisch out of the suite, down the corridor, and to the elevator. They pushed the button. Almost immediately, the door opened. There was one passenger aboard, a tall, well-built, freckle-faced man in a purple turtleneck sweater, a plaid sports coat, yellow trousers and light-brown Earth shoes.

'This elevator is commandeered in the name of the United States Senate,' Senator Fisch said. 'Take us to the scene of the tragic occurrence.'

'*Was hat er gesagt?* What did he say?' the elevator operator asked.

'*Das ist ein United States Senator,*' the passenger replied. '*Alle sind ein bisserl werido.*' (Roughly: 'They are all a bit strange.')

'*Wirklich?*' ('Really?')

'Really. Believe it or not, this is one of the more normal ones.' The passenger switched to English and addressed the senator. 'Get on, Senator. I was going down anyway.'

'It is always a great pleasure and honour to greet one of my fine constituents,' Senator Fisch said, showing his

175

choppers and putting out his hand. The passenger recoiled in horror.

Senator Fisch and Mr. Jambon got in the elevator. The door closed, and the elevator descended to the lobby.

When the door opened, Taylor P. Jambon threw himself into Senator Fisch's arms. Standing in front of the elevator was an enormous bearded man. Sitting beside him, his tail swishing from side to side, was the black Bengal tiger.

'Theosophilus?' the bearded man said in English. 'I may call you Theosophilus?' He spread his arms wide open.

'Boris Alexandrovich?' the passenger said. He spread his arms.

'At long last we meet!' Boris said.

'I have looked forward to finally meeting you, Maestro,* more than you can possibly imagine!'

The passenger, who was, of course, Dr. Theosophilus Mullins Yancey, M.D., Ph.D., D.D. and D.V.M. stepped from the elevator. He was swept up in Boris' arms and raised off the ground. Suddenly Boris stiffened. 'Those two with you, Doc?' he asked suspiciously, having seen the senator and Mr. Jambon.

'My God, no!' the doctor replied.

'I was afraid for a minute . . . I won't even say what I thought,' Boris said. He set the doctor down. 'Doc, I want you to meet the craziest cat in the world. Shake hands with the doc, Baby Brother.'

Baby Brother obediently raised a paw. Dr. Yancey shook it.

'What a splendid animal!' he said. He scratched Baby Brother's ears. Baby Brother rose up on his hind paws. He draped himself on the doctor's shoulders. His tongue came out and licked Dr. Yancey.

'I knew he'd like you,' Boris said. He looked into the elevator, where the senator and Mr. Jambon were still clinging to each other. 'I don't care what your kind does in private,' he said, 'but I can't stand your vulgar exhibitionism in public. Get out of my elevator.'

---

*The press of his professional duties having kept Dr. T. M. Yancey from acquiring a taste for opera, his appelation of 'Maestro' had nothing to do with the singer's musical talents.

'After you, Doctor,' Boris said, bowing the physician-philosopher into the elevator.

'After you, Maestro!' Dr. Yancey replied.

Baby Brother walked into the elevator. Boris and Yancey followed him. As the door closed, Taylor P. Jambon heard the bearded man say, 'I've brought some friends with me. The Baroness d'Iberille and Esmeralda Hoffenburg. I knew that unless I could show you their fantastic muscular control, you wouldn't believe it!'

The door closed, shutting off the rest of the conversation.

Senator Fisch, whose face had taken on sort of a vile green colour, leaned against the wall beside the elevator.

'God has spared me for the good of our beloved country!' he announced.

'Shut up, Jaws,' Taylor P. Jambon said absently. Then, 'Did you see that tiger?'

'Certainly I saw it,' the senator replied. 'What do you think made me wet my pants?'

'We can use that cat,' Taylor P. Jambon said. 'I can see it now.'

'You don't have to draw attention to it, Taylor P. It could have happened to anybody,' the senator replied, modestly crossing his hands over a dark area in the vicinity of the juncture of his trunk and legs.

'Saintly Miss Patience Throckbottom Worthington,' Taylor P. Jambon said, 'sitting in a rocking chair, like Whistler's mother, her gentle, white hand stroking that tiger's head, while she makes the APPLE pitch.' He looked at Senator Fisch. 'You go change your pants, Jaws,' he said. 'I'm going to find out who that tiger belongs to.'

He walked over to the desk.

'Say,' he said, 'I'm Taylor P. Jambon, the famous gourmet and animal lover.'

'Indeed?'

'I wouldn't say so if it wasn't true,' Taylor P. went on. 'Tell me, my good man, who was that who just got on the elevator?'

'I'm afraid I don't know who you mean, sir,' the desk clerk replied. He had been briefed, of course, both by security officers from the Ministry of culture and by the general manager of the hotel. The presence of Boris Alexandrovich Korsky-Rimsakov in the Bristol Hotel was not only a state secret but a secret which the hotel intended to guard with its very life. They knew full well what havoc the singer's fans could cause in their frenzied attempts to gaze upon his face or touch his hand.

'I mean the great big guy with the beard,' Taylor P. Jambon said. 'That's who I mean.'

'I'm afraid I don't know who you mean, sir,' the desk clerk replied.

'He had a tiger with him,' Taylor P. said. 'A big black tiger that shook hands.'

'You don't say?' the desk clerk said.

'And you didn't see him?' Taylor P. pursued.

'I'm afraid I didn't notice, sir,' the desk clerk said.

Taylor P. Jambon, somewhat confused, turned around for support. There was no one in the lobby at all. He turned back to the desk clerk.

'You can't get away with fooling Taylor P. Jambon,' he said. 'I'll get that cat on my APPLE appeals if it's the last thing I do.'

He strode to the elevator and gave his floor number. As soon as the elevator door closed, the front door of the hotel swung inward. Six robed Arabs strode quickly inside, swinging their submachine guns menacingly around the interior.

When the elevator door finally closed all the way and the elevator began to rise, Taylor P. Jambon looked skyward.

'God wasn't saving you, Jaws,' he said fervently. 'He was saving me.'

The desk clerk pushed a button, ringing a bell in the general manager's office. That luminary came rushing out. He rushed up to a seventh, rather portly Arab, who was accompanied by two women, bowed, clicked his heels and bowed again.

'Your Royal Highness,' he said. 'Ladies, welcome to the Bristol Hotel.'

'Has the Maestro arrived safely?' Hassan asked.

'He just a moment ago joined Dr. Yancey,' the desk clerk announced, clicking his heels and bowing. 'They are in the doctor's suite.'

'If you will be good enough to show the baroness and Fräulein Hoffenburg up?' Prince Hassan said. 'They are expected.'

'With the greatest of pleasure, Your Royal Highness,' the desk clerk said.

'There has been a slight change in our requirements,' Prince Hassan said.

'You won't be needing all the hotel, Your Royal Highness?' the manager asked, his face falling. Not only did His Royal Highness never question the bill, but he always paid, daily, with little bags of gold coins.

'I believe my chargé d'affaires asked you to prepare for the Maestro's dog?'

'And such a splendid animal,' the manager gushed. 'It shook hands like a little gentleman.'

Hassan looked at him oddly. 'That wasn't the Maestro's dog,' he said. 'That was the duchess' tiger.'

'How stupid of me!' the manager said.

'Not at all,' Hassan said. 'The tiger thinks he's a dog. How were you to know?'

'You are most gracious, Your Royal Highness. The Maestro's dog won't be coming?'

'Just as soon as my men can get him out of the car,' Hassan said. 'He's sulking. His feelings were hurt when the Maestro locked him in the washroom while he was exercising.'

'Then what seems to be the problem, Your Royal Highness?'

'There will be ten dogs in all,' Hassan said. There was a noise at the door. Hassan turned. 'Ah, here they are!'

Her Grace the Duchess of Folkestone and Mr. Angus MacKenzie, V.C., strode through the door. Mr. MacKenzie had Babykins and Wee Black Runt on his leash. Her Grace had Prince and Wee Black Doggie XIV on hers.

Babykins and Wee Black Runt sniffed the air. Their keen noses detected the peculiar odour of their adopted son and

179

brother, Wee Baby Brother, from whom they had been separated at the railway station. Giving off happy yelps, they lowered their noses and followed the scent across the lobby. Mr. MacKenzie got a good grip on the leash, leaned back and braced himself. He looked something like a beginning water-skier as they dragged him across the lobby.

The manager hurriedly climbed up on the marble counter by the desk, watching in horror as MacKenzie skied through the potted palms on his way to the elevator.

'What's the matter?' Hassan asked. 'You do like dogs, don't you?'

'I just *love* dogs, Your Royal Highness,' the manager said. He smiled bravely. For this, he thought, he was certainly entitled to the Hotelier's Medal of Honour for Valour in the Face of Insurmountable Difficulty.

Suddenly, a shriek filled the lobby. All eyes snapped towards the elevator.

Patience Throckbottom Worthington, her broken leg stuck straight out in front of her wheelchair, had set out to find dear Boris. Her elevator had deposited her in the lobby just in time for Babykins and Wee Black Runt to meet it.

Senator Cacciatore had sent to Miss Worthington, as a token of the esteem he and Mrs. Cacciatore felt for America's most beloved thespian, two dozen long-stemmed roses. ('Why not *two* dozen?' he had reasoned. 'I'm sure the American people would not wish their chairman of the Senate Ad Hoc Committee to Investigate the Mistreatment of Kangaroos and Other Innocent Beasts to be niggardly with their money.')

'I knew that bleeping Jambon ignoramus couldn't be trusted,' Miss Worthington screamed, swinging the roses like a club at Babykins and Wee Black Runt. 'These bleeping carnivores think I'm their bleeping supper.'

The dogs, in the mistaken belief that the nice lady with the funny white leg wanted to play with them, barked happily. This also served to drown out Miss Worthington's comment. There was just time, as Babykins and Wee Black Runt backed up, preparatory to jumping, for Miss Worthington to

180

throw the roses out of the elevator, grab her cane and push the elevator button. The door whooshed closed.

Angus MacKenzie stood there while the dogs leaped happily at the door, with two dozen long-stemmed roses in his arms.

'Angus,' the dowager duchess inquired icily, 'do you know that woman?'

'No, Dumpling,' Mr. MacKenzie replied. 'Never saw her before.'

'Then why did she give you roses?' the duchess asked. 'Angus, how *could* you?'

Franz Schubert von und zu Gurkelhausen, who had been seeing to the luggage, entered the lobby of the hotel. He saw the manager standing on the marble counter by the desk.

'Why are you standing on the counter?' he asked.

The manager was saved from the dilemma of answering an unanswerable question by the ringing of the telephone. He grabbed it, listened a moment, and handed it to Franzl.

'It is for you, Excellency,' he said. 'It is the chief of customs at Schwechat Airfield.'

'Franz Schubert von und zu Gurkelhausen,' he said to the telephone.

'You are the Franz Schubert von und zu Gurkelhausen who is deputy chief of protocol?'

'Of course I am,' Franzl replied. 'How many Franz Schubert von und zu Gurkelhausens do you think there are?'

'Excellency,' the man from Schwechat said, 'a very strange airplane has just landed out here.'

'What's so strange about it?'

'Well, there's a lady dressed like an archbishop, and she has five black bears with her.'

'What do you mean?' Franzl spluttered. 'A lady dressed like an archbishop?'

The Dowager Duchess of Folkestone walked over to Franzl.

'Dutch,' she said, 'did I hear you say a lady dressed like an archbishop?'

Franzl nodded dumbly.

'That must be Reverend Mother,' the dowager duchess

said. 'Thank God she's here!' She snatched the phone from Franzl. 'Put the lady on,' she ordered. There was a pause. 'What do you mean, who am I? I'm the dowager duchess of Folkestone, that's who I am!' There was another pause, then: 'Hot Lips? Florabelle. Oh, Hot Lips, I'm so glad you're here. I need your counsel. Angus has been carrying on behind my back with a red-headed harridan in a wheelchair.' Pause. 'Of course, I'm sure. She just gave him two dozen long-stemmed roses right before my very eyes.' Pause. 'I'll be waiting, Hot Lips,' she said and then hung up. She turned to Mr. MacKenzie: 'You'd better think of a good story for Reverend Mother, you kilted Don Juan!' she said. 'She's on her way from the airport!'

'Florabelle!' Angus said. 'Dumpling!'

'Don't you "Dumpling" me, you scoundrel!' the dowager duchess said. 'And with Woody and Beverly due here any minute!'

She snatched the leash holding Babykins and Wee Black Runt from his hands and, dragging them and Prince and Wee Black Doggie XIV after her, got on the elevator.

'Shame on you!' she said, and then the elevator door closed.

Angus MacKenzie turned to Franzl.

'Dutch,' he said, 'kin ye tell me what the hell happened?'

'Vienna,' Franzl replied, 'is the city of love. Sometimes it gets out of hand.' He winked at Mr. MacKenzie and jabbed him, one man-of-the-world to another, in the ribs.

'Is there a bar in this place?' Mr. MacKenzie inquired.

'Right through that door, sir,' the manager said.

'If anybody should ask, which seems highly unlikely, that's where I'll be,' Mr. MacKenzie said.

There was no one in the bar when Angus first climbed onto a stool and asked for a wee drop of Royal Highland Dew Straight Scots Whisky. About five minutes later, however, another customer appeared. He, too, seemed a bit distraught. He ordered a triple bourbon, tossed it down at a gulp, and ordered another.

'American, aren't ye?' Angus said. 'I kin tell by the funny accent ye have.'

'You're the first Austrian I've met who speaks English,' Taylor P. Jambon replied.

'I'm not an Austrian, I'm a Scot!' Angus somewhat huffily corrected him.

'No offence intended,' Taylor P. Jambon said with all the charm he could muster. Angus MacKenzie was a large man who looked quite capable of physical violence, and Taylor P. Jambon loathed violence. 'Might I have the great privilege of buying you a drink?'

'Ye may,' Angus replied. 'MacKenzie's the name.'

'Jambon,' Mr. Jambon said, 'Taylor P. Jambon.'

The door suddenly flung open. The Reverend Mother Emeritus Margaret H. W. Wilson stepped inside. She flung her cape over her shoulder and pointed her shepherd's crook at Angus.

'Angus!' she said. 'I'm shocked!'

'There's two sides to every story, Hot Lips,' Angus said.

'And here you sit, drinking whisky at eleven o'clock in the morning!'

'That I am,' Angus said. 'Would you like a little snort yerself, Hot Lips?'

'Perhaps,' Reverend Mother, hoisting herself onto a stool, 'just a drop to cut the dust, as Colonel Beauregard Beaucoupmots is wont to say.'

'This gentleman is buying,' Angus said, nodding at Taylor P. Jambon. 'Ain't you?' He explained. 'He's making up for not recognizing me right off as a Scot.'

'My pleasure,' Taylor P. Jambon said.

'A teensy weensy little Scotch,' Hot Lips said to the bartender. She indicated the quantity she wished by holding her thumb and index finger just as far apart as they would go. 'And go light on the water,' she added.

'Madam,' Taylor P. Jambon replied, 'might I ever so politely inquire what exactly it is that you're dressed up for?'

'As any fool can plainly see,' Angus MacKenzie said, 'you are speaking with the Reverend Mother Emeritus of the God Is Love in All Forms Christian Church, Inc.'

'Of course,' Taylor P. Jambon said. 'I should have known that right away.'

'This reverend lady united me and Florabelle in holy wedlock,' Angus said.

'And now you have strayed, Angus, from the bonds of wedded bliss?' Hot Lips asked.

'Hot Lips, I swear I have never seen that lady before in my life,' Angus said fervently. 'I have been true to Florabelle!'

'Then why did she give you two dozen roses?' Hot Lips said.

'Well, Hot Lips,' Angus said, 'you know how it is. We Scots have always had a certain attraction for the lasses.'

'Angus,' Hot Lips said, downing her drink and signalling for a refill, 'I know how it is!'

'It's not that I wouldn't be interested, Hot Lips,' Angus said. 'But I am, as ye well know, having tied the knot, so to speak, yerself, that I am a married man, with my oat-sowing far behind me.'

'That's not what I meant, Angus,' Hot Lips said, blushing prettily. 'What I meant to say is that I know what it is to be nothing more than a sex symbol, to be pursued, to be the unwilling object of attention.'

'Me, too,' Taylor P. Jambon said. 'I'll drink to that.'

'Angus,' Hot Lips said, 'I believe you. I know you wouldn't lie to Reverend Mother.'

'Absolutely not,' Angus said. 'I'm as pure as the fallen snow.'

'Don't go overboard,' Reverend Mother said. 'But I will go speak with Florabelle and tell her her fears are groundless.'

'I'd be grateful to ye, Hot Lips,' Angus said.

'Me, too, Hot Lips,' Taylor P. Jambon said.

'Reverend Mother to you, Lardbelly,' Reverend Mother said. She tossed her drink down and picked up her shepherd's crook. 'I go now, to restore you to the bosom of your bride,' she said.

'You're a good woman, Hot Lips,' Angus said.

'I'll drink to that,' Taylor P. Jambon said.

Hot Lips swept out of the bar. Angus turned to Taylor P. Jambon.

'You don't hold your liquor too well, do ye?' he said. 'You

184

really had one hell of a nerve calling Reverend Mother "Hot Lips". I suppose ye know that?'

'No offence intended,' Taylor P. Jambon said. 'I've had a trying day.' He signalled the bartender for another round.

'Yer still buying, of course?' Angus asked.

'Absolutely,' Mr. Jambon said. 'Say, could I ask you a question?'

'Since yer buying, why not?'

'What would you say if I told you there was a guy in the hotel lobby a while back with a tame Bengal tiger?'

'That's be Wee Baby Brother,' Angus said.

'Wee Baby Brother?'

'He thinks he's a dog, poor pussycat,' Angus explained.

'You mean you know who owns this animal?' Taylor P. inquired, brightening considerably.

'Me Florabelle owns him,' Angus said. 'Me and Florabelle together.'

'Your Florabelle,' Taylor P. Jambon inquired, by now willing to believe anything, 'is a rather enormous bearded gentleman?'

'I suppose that's what you call American humour,' Angus said. 'I dinna think yer drunk enough to be looking for a fight wi' me.'

'Perish the thought,' Taylor P. Jambon said. 'I am obviously mistaken.'

'What are ye so concerned about Wee Baby Brother for?'

'Tell me, Mr. MacKenzie,' Taylor P. Jambon said. 'Have you ever heard of APPLE?'

'We eat apples in Scotland, just like everyplace else,' Angus said.

'This is a different kind of apple. It stands for the Association of Pup and Pussy Lovers in Earnest.'

'An organization of animal lovers?' Angus inquired.

'Precisely,' Taylor P. Jambon said.

'Ye dinna look the type,' Angus said. 'But if yer helping pups and pussies, I'm on yer side.'

'We go on television and ask other people to help us,' Taylor P. went on.

'That seems to be a verra sensible thing to do,' Angus said.

185

'And what I was thinking, Mr. MacKenzie, is that I would like to use your tiger in one of our commercials. America's most beloved thespian, Miss Patience Throckbottom Worthington, has graciously agreed to help our noble cause. What I would like to do is show her petting your tiger while she talks. How does that strike you?'

'If Hot Lips succeeds in fixing things with Florabelle, I'll ask her,' Angus replied.

'You're a good man, Mr. MacKenzie.'

'I know,' Angus said. 'I've always had that same idea.'

CHAPTER SEVENTEEN

Every family, some wise man once said, has its skeleton. In the case of the happy family of the News Department of the Amalgamated Broadcasting System, there were two skeletons. These were 'Trench Coat Wally' Michaels and Harley Hazardous.

No one knew how they come to be on the ABS payroll, and it was even more mysterious how they stayed on it.* Trench Coat Wally and Harley were hardly team players. Not only had they been heard to laugh out loud while viewing 'Waldo Maldemer and the Evening News With Don Rhotten', which was heresy tantamount to advocating pay television, but they had even turned their journalistic endeavours on their co-workers at ABS News itself. Their weekly programme 'One Hour', aired on prime time Sunday evenings, had been the only television news show to air film of Don Rhotten and Congressman Edwards L. 'Smiling Jack' Jackson emerging from the Casablanca, Morocco, Bastille, for example.

For reasons that no one but the chairman of the board understood, they had carte blanche to travel the world and do what they wished. Their film was sent to New York and aired, without censorship of any kind, on 'One Hour'. Not only was this in keeping with the highest standards of TV journalism, the chairman of the board had concluded, but it kept them from nosing around massage parlours in New York.

---

*The truth of the matter, well hidden of course, was that while Michaels and Hazardous were doing a story on Manhattan massage parlours, early on in their careers, they had shot some very interesting film of an enthusiastic massagee who happened to be vice-chairman of the board of ABS. They had had the journalistic foresight not to turn the film in. From time to time, however, when leaned upon, they showed it to the vice-chairman of the board. This always served to remind the vice-chairman (later the chairman) of the sacred obligation of television journalism to present the truth, the whole truth, and nothing but the truth, without fear of favour.

They worked independently, seldom meeting face to face. But as the same wise man who said that every family had its skeleton said, so do the paths of all men cross at one time or another. So it was at Schwechat that Harley Hazardous, en route from Moscow via Vienna to New Delhi, looked up from his *frankfurter mit sauerkraut* in the Transient Lounge to stare into a familiar face, this one stuffing itself with a *sachertorte mit schlagobers*.*

It was, of course (you could tell by the trench coat), Trench Coat Wally Michaels, who was en route from Teheran, via Vienna, to Tokyo.

'Hello, there, Trench Coat Wally,' Harley Hazardous said. 'What brings you to wherever we are?'

'Well, as I live and breathe, if it isn't Harley Hazardous himself,' Trench Coat Wally said. 'It's a small world, ain't it?'

'Where are you going?' Harley Hazardous asked.

'Tokyo,' Trench Coat Wally replied. 'Where are you going?'

'New Delhi,' Harley Hazardous said. 'Why are you going to Tokyo? *I* was there last week.'

'And I was in New Delhi, let me see, day before yesterday. Why are you going there?'

'I didn't know,' Harley said.

'Either did I,' Trench Coat Wally said.

'It was bound to happen, I suppose,' Harley said.

'Sooner or later, we were going to run out of exotic cities.'

'Well, what do we do now?' Harley asked.

'Jeez, I don't know,' Trench Coat Wally replied.

'What do you say we take a couple of days off?'

'You mean it?' Wally asked.

'Why not?'

'Where did you say we are?'

Harley Hazardous looked around for a sign and found one. 'Wine,' he said.

'That's *Wien*, Harley; it means Vienna,' Trench Coat Wally said.

*A Viennese delicacy, 2,000 calories to the ounce, consisting of a layered chocolate cake buried in whipped cream.

'Oh!' Harley said, delighted. 'I remember Vienna. Blonde girls.'

'Right.'

'Let's find a cab,' Trench Coat Wally said. 'To hell with New Delhi.'

'To hell with Tokyo,' Harley Hazardous said. 'All work and no play makes Harley a dull boy.'

Trench Coat Wally consulted a small notebook. 'The best hotel in town is the Sacher.'

'The Sacher it is,' Harley Hazardous said. They left the Transient Lounge, picked up their bags and looked for a cab. As they waited, they saw a fork lift truck unloading familiar wooden cases. They bore the familiar ABS logo-type, a human ear with a television camera sticking out of it.

'That your equipment, Harley?' Trench Coat Wally asked.

'Must be yours, Wally,' Harley replied. 'I sent my crew ahead to New Delhi. I got in a poker game with Kosygin, and he didn't want to quit.'

'It's not mine,' Trench Coat Wally replied. 'I played a couple of rounds of golf with the Shah and sent my crew ahead to Tokyo.'

Their journalistic curiosity aroused, they examined the crates.

FOR DON RHOTTEN
HOTEL MAJESTIC
VIENNA, AUSTRIA

'I wonder what that Rotten Don's doing in Vienna,' Harley Hazardous said.

'I don't know,' Trench Coat Wally said. 'But if he's going to be in Vienna, I want to be someplace else.'

'Ordinarily, Wally,' Harley Hazardous said, 'I would agree with you.'

'You usually do,' Wally said modestly.

'But, in an idle moment between Timbuktu and Pazarhdzik, Bulgaria, I had time to think.'

'About what?'

'You-know-who, Wally, is at that age when getting caught

189

in a massage parlour is a matter of pride rather than embarrassment.'

'You're right,' Wally said.

'I usually am,' Harley Hazardous said. 'The obvious conclusion is that we need something else in our little vault to keep you-know-who in line.'

'What's the bottom line, Harley?'

'Rotten Don is bound to do something here that would embarrass the network if it was on film,' Harley said.

'As usual, Harley, you're onto something,' Trench Coat Wally said. 'But we don't have any equipment.'

Harley Hazardous was already prying open one of the crates. The first crate was useless. All it contained was Don Rhotten's dressing table and spare toupees. The second crate, however, contained just what they wanted — a portable camera and a battery-powered tape recorder.

'This's going to be just like old times, Harley,' Trench Coat Wally said.

'Yeah,' Harley agreed, 'before we did our show on the massage parlours.'

A cab appeared.

'The Hotel Sacher,' Harley ordered, and in great good spirits they climbed in and were driven off.

Thirty minutes later, having checked into the Hotel Sacher and needing sustenance, they ventured out onto Kärntner-strasse. They carried with them, of course, the camera and the tape recorder.

'Hey, Harley,' Trench Coat Wally said, hastily winding the camera, 'look at that. A big guy with a tame tiger.'

'That's not news, Wally,' Harley said. 'It's obviously an advertisement for a circus.' But Harley turned on his tape recorder anyway, and they ran down the street after Boris, Dr. Yancy and Wee Baby Brother.

The Maestro, of course, knew Vienna, and he headed unerringly for the restaurant he loved above all others, the Wolfgang Amadeus Mozart Paprika Goulash Parlour.

Despite the presence of Wee Baby Brother (after all, he was the Maestro and entitled to an idiosyncrasy or two), he was greeted warmly by the proprietor and greeted him

190

warmly in turn. He picked him up and spun him around. When he spun him around, he saw Trench Coat Wally with the camera to his eye.

'Excuse me, sir,' he said in faultless German, 'is that a motion-picture camera of the type used by news media?'

Herr Joseph Haydn Kramer, the proprietor of the Wolfgang Amadeus Mozart Paprika Goulash Parlour, paled. He knew the Maestro quite well, and he knew that when the Maestro simply oozed with charm and courtesy, a brawl followed as invariably as the dawn follows the night.

'What did he say?' Harley Hazardous asked.

'I don't know. I don't speak German.'

'Forgive me,' Boris said, this time in English, oozing charm. 'I had the temerity to inquire if that device you hold before you is a motion-picture camera of the type used by the television news media?'

'Why do you ask?' Trench Coat Wally said.

'If it were, sir,' Boris said, putting the proprietor down and picking up Trench Coat Wally, 'I would make you eat it.'

'You put Trench Coat Wally down, you big ape!' Harley Hazardous said. Boris had been holding Trench Coat Wally with both hands. He let one hand go and used it to pick up Harley Hazardous.

'You were saying, Little Man?'

'What exactly is it you have against the television news media?' Trench Coat Wally asked, rather politely.

'You look to me, sir,' Boris said, 'as if you might be a friend and associate of Don Rhotten, America's most beloved telecaster.'

When in doubt, as Trench Coat Wally Michaels always said, 'Tell the truth.'

'Not really,' he said.

'Oh?'

'As a matter of fact, I can't stand him,' Wally plunged ahead.

'Perhaps I have misjudged you,' Boris said and put him down. 'And you, Chubby?'

'I don't like him either,' Harley Hazardous said. He was set back on his feet.

'Sir,' Trench Coat Wally said, 'if it could be arranged, how would you like to pick up Rotten Don Rhotten the way you just picked up me and my friend?'

'Good thinking, Wally,' Harley Hazardous said.

'Why would I want to do that?' Boris asked.

'Possibly, you might wish to throw him someplace,' Trench Coat Wally said. 'Maybe into the fountain in the park.'

'I think I like you,' Boris said. 'Permit me to introduce myself. I am Boris Alexandrovich Korsky-Rimsakov.'

While neither Trench Coat Wally nor Harley could truly be considered opera buffs, they recognized the name.

'The opera singer?'

'The world's greatest opera singer, actually,' Boris said. 'And this is my friend and fellow sociobiological scientist, Dr. T. Mullins Yancey, otherwise known as the Sage of Manhattan, Kansas.'

As the men shook hands, Boris pointed at Joseph Haydn Kramer. 'A bottle of your finest slivovitz,* Joseph!' he said. 'And some glasses.'

'My name,' Trench Coat Wally said, with becoming modesty, 'is Wally Michaels, and this is my co-worker, Harley Hazardous.' Their programme was, after all, watched by some forty-million people every Sunday night. It was reasonable to assume that his face and name would be known.

'How do you do?' Boris said. 'Tourists, are you?'

'Not really,' Wally said gingerly.

'The truth of the matter is, sir,' Harley said, 'that we are television journalists . . .'

'Hold the slivovitz!' Boris bellowed.

'Poor, struggling, honest TV journalists,' Trench Coat Wally said, suddenly inspired, 'denied our proper place by such as the likes of Rotten Don Rhotten.'

'They're all right, Boris,' Dr. Yancey said. 'I watch them all the time.'

* Slivovitz is brandy made from Hungarian plums. As a general rule of thumb, two ounces of slivovitz equals, in potency, one pint of French brandy.

'You have just been vouched for by the world's greatest sex expert,' Boris said. 'Serve the slivovitz, Joseph!'

Wee Baby Brother, while all this was going on, had been sitting quietly, swishing his tail from side to side. Suddenly, he rose up on all fours and appeared to be staring (his head cocked from side to side) with rapt fascination at Harley Hazardous.

'Nice pussy!' Hazardous said.

Wee Baby Brother was not, in fact, staring at Harley Hazardous and didn't pay him a bit of attention even after Harley snatched a Wiener schnitzel from the plate of a diner at the adjacent table and held it out to him.

Wee Baby Brother's sensitive ears had heard a familiar sound. He raised his head and barked.

'What's he doing? What's he doing?' Harley inquired, rather faintly.

'He's barking,' Boris said. 'He thinks he's a dog.'

'Isn't that interesting?' Harley Hazardous whispered. '*Nice* doggie!'

'Sit down, Wee Baby Brother,' Boris said, 'and behave yourself.'

Wee Baby Brother disobeyed. He raised his head and barked again. In a moment, the reason became apparent. The door to the restaurant crashed open. What looked to Harley Hazardous and Trench Coat Wally like five black bears came rushing in, dragging behind them three men, one of whom had his arm in a cast. Harley Hazardous looked at his hand, holding the Wiener schnitzel, and quickly dropped it.

'No wonder he was excited,' Boris said as the largest of the dogs, snapping his leash, jumped over the table from which Harley had stolen the schnitzel and jumped in Boris' lap. 'Don't be jealous, Prince,' he said. 'Daddy loves you too!' He turned his head and bellowed. 'Bring another bottle, and some more glasses!'

'Dr. Yancey, I presume?' Hawkeye said, extending his hand. 'Fancy meeting you here in the heart of darkest Austria.'

'I don't believe I've had the pleasure,' Dr. Yancy said.

'Trapper John McIntyre,' Trapper John said. 'Pleased to

make your acquaintance. Say hello to Dick Wilson, famous one-handed apprentice cutter.'

'How do you do, Doctor?' Dr. Wilson said. 'I've heard so much about you.' (This was something of an understatement.)

'How did you guys find me?' Boris asked.

'It was easy,' Hawkeye said. 'We just walked out of the hotel, turned right, and asked the first man we saw had he seen a bearded monster with a tame tiger.'

'I thought Horsey was coming, too,' Boris said.

'He went out to the airport to meet Woody and Dick's girlfriend,' Hawkeye said. He looked suspiciously at Harley Hazardous and Trench Coat Wally Michaels. 'I don't mean to insult you,' he said, 'but has anyone ever told you you two look just like a couple of boob-tube sages?'

'They're all right, Hawkeye,' Boris said. 'They can't stand Don Rhotten, either.'

'You mean it really is them?' Hawkeye asked.

'In the flesh,' Boris said, and pointed at Harley Hazardous. 'In this case, a lot of it.'

'He's here you know,' Trapper John said. 'He was coming into the hotel as we left. He was disguised. But it wasn't, you will recall, the first time I'd seen him without his wig, caps and contacts, and I recognized him right away.'

'He didn't say what he was up to, by any chance?' Trench Coat Wally asked.

'He was awfully upset,' Hawkeye said. 'Somebody apparently stole one of his cameras and one of his tape recorders.'

'Nothing is sacred these days,' Trench Coat Wally observed.

'But what's he up to?' Harley Hazardous asked.

'That's really what we're doing here,' Trapper John said. 'He wants to take some film of Wee Baby Brother. We came to get him.'

'Not on your life!' Boris promptly replied.

'It's for a good cause,' Trapper said. 'That's what Taylor P. Jambon told Angus. So it's certainly something rotten. The problem is, what?'

'APPLE,' Trench Coat Wally repeated. 'The Association of Pup and Pussy Lovers in Earnest. That's what it must be,' he said.

'But how can you be so sure?' Trapper asked. 'That sounds like a perfectly respectable organization.'

'Let me put it this way,' Trench Coat Wally said. 'If the boss is Taylor P. Jambon and it's being pushed by Rotten Don Rhotten, how could it possibly be honest?'

'Good thinking, Wally,' Harley Hazardous said. 'But what, exactly?'

'I don't know,' Wally confessed. 'But my sniffer tells me that I'm onto a story.'

'And your sniffer is never wrong, right?' Harley replied.

'I've got the best nose for news in the business,' Trench Coat Wally said. 'You know that, Harley.'

'The reddest, too, I'll bet,' Trapper John chimed in.

'But how are we going to foil their nefarious plot unless we know what it is?' Hawkeye asked.

'I'll make a deal with you guys,' Trench Coat Wally said. 'If the big fella here promises to throw Don Rhotten into that big fountain so that we can get a picture of it . . .'

'With or without his wig?' Hawkeye asked.

'Maybe you could arrange it to have it come off in flight,' Harley Hazardous suggested.

'You got it,' Boris said. 'Now what are you going to do for us?'

'We will put our joint journalistic noses to snooping out what Don Rhotten is up to,' Trench Coat Walley said. 'Fair enough?'

'You got a deal,' Boris said. 'Let's have a drink on it.' He bellowed: 'Another bottle, Joseph!'

'Are the first two gone already?' Dr. Yancey asked.

'Might I be excused?' Dr. Wilson asked.

'First door on the left,' Boris said. 'It says "Herren" on the door.'

'That's not what he means, Boris,' Hawkeye said. 'I think he wants to go see if his lady friend is here.'

'I think we'd all better be getting back,' Trapper John said.

'I just got here!' Boris said. 'I need sustenance.'

'You can get sustenance at the dinner the Austrians are throwing for you. You just have time to dress.'

'Tell them I'm not coming,' Boris said with finality. 'I'd rather booze it up with you guys.'

'The duchess is looking forward to it,' Hawkeye said, 'and so are Hot Lips and Beverly. You're going, Boris, and reasonably sober.'

Meanwhile, back at the Bristol Hotel:

'I'd like to thank you for getting us these rooms,' Seymour G. Schwartz said to Senator J. Ellwood 'Jaws' Fisch.

'Think nothing of it, sir,' the senator replied. 'The Ad Hoc Committee's paying for them.'

'Generally,' Seymour G. Schwartz said, 'it's difficult finding rooms in hotels with six topless desk persons waiting around the lobby for something exciting to happen.'

Don Rhotten, who had been staring with obvious approval at his reflection in the mirror, suddenly snapped to attention.

'Topless desk persons?' he asked. 'I didn't see any topless desk persons!'

'I saw them,' Seymour G. Schwartz said. 'Didn't you see them, Taylor?'

'I saw them,' Taylor P. Jambon quickly agreed, 'three brunettes, a redhead and two blondes.' He didn't know where Mr. Schwartz was going (they had, in fact, just a minute before met for the first time), but he was obviously cut from the same cloth.

'Fascinating!' Senator Fisch said.

'I heard the redhead say that she was just thrilled that there was a U.S. senator in the hotel,' Seymour said.

'I thought that was one of the blondes,' Taylor P. Jambon said.

'No, the blonde said that she was even more excited because Don Rhotten was supposed to be in the hotel.'

'She said that, did she?' Don Rhotten said, sticking his thumb in his eye to make sure the Paul Newman—blue contact lens was in straight.

'If you gentlemen can see your way clear to excusing me,' Senator Fisch said, 'I think I'll take a little stroll.'

196

'Me, too,' Don Rhotten said.

Seymour G. Schwartz turned to Taylor P. Jambon. They exchanged a significant look but said nothing until the senator and Don Rhotten had gone.

'You handled that very well,' Taylor P. Jambon said.

'I thought so, Mr. Jambon,' Mr. Schwartz replied 'Now, shall we get down to business?'

'Why, I'm not sure I know what you mean, Mr. Schwartz,' Taylor P. Jambon said. He had a sudden sure sensation that he wasn't going to like this at all.

'This is Seymour G. Schwartz you're dealing with, not that dummy senator of yours,' Seymour said. 'You didn't really think you were going to get Don Rhotten for free, did you?'

'Whatever do you mean?'

'We want thirty per cent of the take,' Seymour said. 'Clear enough?'

Taylor P. Jambon's smile vanished. 'Clear enough,' he said. 'But thirty per cent is out of the question.'

'Tell me why,' Seymour G. Schwartz said.

'Well, for one thing, despite what the publicity said about her doing it for the love of animals, I had to pay Patience Throckbottom Worthington a bundle. Not to mention her hospital bill.'

'Let's get down to figures,' Seymour said.

'I'll lay it all out on the table for you,' Taylor P. Jambon said. 'The way we have it figured, what with administrative and operating expenses, we're going to be lucky to break even.'

'How much do the dogs and cats get?'

'Ten per cent,' Taylor P. Jambon said. 'That's after operating and administrative expenses, of course.'

'Since we need thirty per cent, that leaves us with the problem of taking twenty per cent from administrative and operating expenses,' Seymour G. Schwartz said.

'You mean, you're going to take the pups's and pussycats' ten per cent?'

'Who's to know?' Seymour G. Schwartz said. 'They can't talk, you know.'

'O.K.,' Taylor P. said. 'Scratch the ten per cent for the

197

dogs and cats. But you don't expect me or the senator to give up our consultant's fees and expense accounts, do you?'

'Give them up? No. Whittle them down a little. Certainly. What does your consultant's fees and expenses come to, percentage-wise?'

'A little over fifty per cent,' Taylor P. Jambon admitted.

'It just dropped to forty,' Seymour G. Schwartz said. 'Where can we get the other ten per cent?'

'Noplace,' Taylor P. Jambon said, obviously telling the truth. 'Forty per cent goes for direct-mailing expenses, typewriters, office supplies. That sort of thing.'

'Some of your employees are about to take a cut in salary,' Seymour G. Schwartz said.

'You don't really think I pay them, do you?' Taylor P. Jambon replied. 'They're volunteers, Seymour. Free volunteers. You know the type, kooks and nuts who really like dogs and cats.'

'Very clever of you,' Seymour said. 'You're smarter than you look, Taylor P.'

'Thank you,' Taylor P. said. 'From you, that's a real compliment.'

'I'll split the difference with you,' Seymour said, 'as a token of my affection and respect. The cut for you and the senator is down to thirty per cent. Our cut is thirty per cent. Expenses are forty per cent. That adds up to one hundred per cent.'

'Just for the record, we should spend something on the dogs and cats.'

'Take it out of your share,' Seymour said. 'What have dogs and cats ever done for me?'

'Be a sport, Seymour,' Taylor P. said. 'Besides, what if it ever got out that the damned dogs and cats weren't getting any of it?'

'You have a point,' Seymour said, after thinking it over. 'I'm a reasonable man. One per cent from my share, one per cent from your share. That's two whole per cent for the animals. What could be fairer?'

'You're a man after my own heart, Seymour,' Taylor P. Jambon said, putting out his hand.

'Just to satisfy my curiosity, Taylor P.,' Seymour said, 'what are you going to do with all the money we're going to give the cats and dogs?'

'It's rather indelicate,' Taylor P. said, 'it has to do with fixing them so they can't have any little cats, if you follow my meaning.'

'The dogs, too?'

'The dogs, too, of course,' Taylor P. Jambon said. 'That's how I got into this good work, incidentally. I had a cat. She had no morals at all, I'm ashamed to say. Well, I had to have her fixed. I was going broke buying cat food. And you wouldn't believe what it cost. So I got to thinking, why should *I* pay for it?'

'So what did you do?'

'I started APPLE, of course,' Taylor P. said with quiet modesty. 'I knew, of course, from my career as a gourmet, that you can tell people anything and get them to believe it.'

'You're a clever man, Taylor P.,' Seymour G. Schwartz said. 'Almost but not quite, as clever as I am.'

CHAPTER EIGHTEEN

'Mr. Ambassador,' his secretary said, breaking the news as gently as she could, 'Senator Cacciatore is on the telephone.'

'Splendid!' the ambassador said, forcing a smile and reaching for the instrument. He took a deep breath, forced an even wider smile, and took the handset from the cradle. 'Good afternoon, Senator!' He said enthusiastically. 'How good of me to call you. I mean, of course, how good of *you* to call me!'

'I'm calling on behalf of my wife and myself, and, of course, on behalf of Senator Fisch,' Senator Cacciatore said.

'Oh?'

'To express my deep gratitude for all that you've done for us,' the senator went on.

'Well, how nice of you.'

'And just as soon as I get back to Washington, Mr. Ambassador, I'm going to bring your splendid performance of duty to the attention of the proper people.'

'That's very kind of you, Senator,' the ambassador said.

'It's not true, you know, just between us, that the chairman of the Senate Committee on Internal Operations and the Chairman of the Senate Committee on Foreign Operations don't like each other.'

'I'm glad to hear that, Senator,' the ambassador said.

'That's what you call a little cosmetics for the folks back home,' Senator Cacciatore said. 'The only reason he called me a goddamned Yankee was for the benefit of the folks back home, you understand?'

'I think so, Senator.'

'And that's why I called him a dumb redneck,' Senator Cacciatore said. 'My constituents like that. The truth of the matter is, Mr. Ambassador, that his neck is as white as yours and mine.'

'Ahhhhhh,' the ambassador said, reluctantly concluding that the truth would come out in the end anyway. 'You are aware, I'm sure, Senator, that I'm an American of African descent?'

'Of *course* I am,' Senator Christopher Columbus Cacciatore said. 'As I was saying to Alabama John – he's the Chairman of the Foreign Operations Committee, you know . . .'

'Yes, Senator, I know,' the ambassador said.

'Alabama John, I said . . . we were having a haircut in the Senate Barbershop at the time . . . 'Alabama John, I want you to know that our ambassador to Austria is a credit to his race.'

'That was very kind of you, Senator,' the ambassador replied.

'Give credit where credit is due, I always say, without regard to creed, colour, or national origin.'

'That's a splendid philosophy, Senator.'

'We Italians are better at that sort of thing than other people, you know,' the senator said. 'It's our Roman heritage. I mean, where would America be if it hadn't been for my namesake, Christopher Columbus?'

The ambassador bit off the reply, 'Off the coast of Ceylon, perhaps?', that came to his lips. 'You're quite right, Senator,' he said. 'Where indeed would it be?'

'What I said to Alabama John, Mr. Ambassador, was before I knew I wasn't invited to the party.'

'I beg your pardon?'

'The next time I see Alabama John, Mr. Ambassador, I'm going to have to qualify what I said before.'

'I don't think I quite follow you, Senator Cacciatore,' the ambassador confessed.

'What I'm going to have to say, I'm afraid, is "Alabama John, what I said about our ambassador to Austria being a credit to his race is good only so far as it goes. When it comes down to getting two U.S. senators, far from home, invited to a party, he's a complete bust. And I say that without reference to his colour, creed or national origin, simply as a statement of fact." That's what I'm going to have to tell my good friend, the distinguished senator from the great state of Alabama.'

201

'What party are we talking about, Senator?' the ambassador asked.

'Put it from your mind,' Senator Cacciatore said. 'Don't give it another thought. We all have our limitations. I have mine, and you have yours, Mr. Ambassador, especially when it comes to getting two United States senators invited to a fancy dinner party. Think nothing more about it. Think about your future. Think how happy you're going to be as second assistant passport officer in the consulate in Zamboanga.'

'Senator,' the ambassador said, 'if you'll only tell me which party it is to which you make reference, perhaps something can be worked out.'

'Worked out? Worked out? You're trying to tell me that maybe, just maybe, you can fix it for two United States senators, members of the most exclusive club in the world, to get invited to some lousy party?'

'Which party, Senator?'

'Since you insist, I personally would never think of going somewhere I wasn't wanted, but since you insist, I'm talking about the party the Australian government is giving for Boris Alexandrovich Korsky-Rimsakov, *that's* what party.'

'The *Australian* government?' the ambassador said.

'Austrian, Australian, what's the difference?' the senator replied. 'The bottom line, you lousy bureaucrat, is that there's going to be a party for Boris Alexandrovich Korsky-Rimsakov, my wife wants to go, and we're not invited. All you diplomats are good for is standing around in striped pants drinking champagne. When it comes to doing something important for your United States senators, you're useless.'

'Senator Cacciatore,' the ambassador said, 'I'm sure there's been some sort of a simple mistake. I'll check into it and get right back to you.'

'Don't bother,' Senator Cacciatore said. 'I wouldn't want you to put yourself out any for a simple servant of the people like myself.'

'It will be my great pleasure, Senator,' the ambassador said. 'I'll get right back to you.'

'If you insist,' Senator Cacciatore said.

The ambassador broke the connection with his finger and told his secretary to get His Excellency Franz Schubert von und zu Gurkelhausen, deputy chief of protocol of the Austrian Foreign Ministry on the line immediately.

'Franzl? Homer.'

'What can I do for you, Homer?'

'Need a little favour, buddy,' Homer said.

'Name it, you got it.'

'You're throwing a little bash tonight for some singer?' There was no reply. 'You hear what I asked, Franzl?'

'I heard, Homer,' Franzl said.

'I need three tickets,' Homer said.

'You don't want to go to that party, Homer,' Franzl said. 'Trust me, you wouldn't like it.'

'They're not for me, Franzl. They're for somebody else.'

'They wouldn't like it either, Homer, believe me.'

'Why not?'

'OK,' Franzl said. 'We're friends. I can tell you the truth, right?'

'Right.'

'There's no more room,' Franzl said. 'That's the bottom line, Homer.'

'What do you mean, no more room?'

'It started out as a nice little supper for twenty,' Franzl said, 'and then it just grew and grew and grew. The way it stands now, the whole restaurant has been taken over for the evening. There's just no more room.'

'Franzl, this is important to me. I need the tickets for two United States senators.'

'I just told the chargé d'affaires of the Russian Embassy there's no tickets, and you're asking me to give tickets to a couple of lousy senators?'

'Plus one for a wife,' the ambassador said.

'Homer . . .'

'Don't Homer me, Franzl,' the ambassador said. 'You owe me. Did I, or didn't I, get you and Frau von und zu Gurkelhausen into Walt Disney World when it was booked solid?'

'You did that,' Franzl admitted.

'And you told me that if there ever was anything you could do for me, all I had to do was ask.'

'I might have said something along those lines,' Franzl admitted.

'Might have? Might have? Are you trying to weasel out of a solemn promise, Franzl?'

'Of course not,' Franzl said. 'I'll get three tickets over to you right away, Homer. But you understand that this evens us up? We're square, even-steven?'

'Send the tickets, Franzl,' the ambassador said.

Franz Schubert von und zu Gurkelhausen called the Drei Hussaren Restaurant's maître d'hôtel.

'Fritzl? Here is Franzl,' he began.

'Don't bother me, von und zu Gurkelhausen, I got three-hundred-sixteen people coming for dinner in an hour.'

'Put in three more chairs, Fritzl,' Franzl said. 'You got three-hundred-nineteen people coming.'

'You're either crazy or drunk,' Fritzl replied. 'There's no more room, period.'

'You've got to make room,' Franzl said. 'That's all there is to it.'

'This is the Drei Hussaren Restaurant, Franzl,' the maître d'hôtel said. 'When people come here to eat, they expect to sit down.'

'Look, the minute it starts, the minute you start with the appetizer, some ladies will go and powder their noses. They always do that, you know they do.'

'So?'

'So when they do, steal their chairs,' Franzl said. 'It's as simple as that.'

'They're not going to notice their chairs are gone?'

'With *Unseren Lieben* Boris at the head table, they wouldn't notice,' Franzl said. 'This isn't the first state dinner you've give for *Unseren Lieben* Boris.'

'I know. We're still repairing the damage for the last one,' Fritzl said. 'I'll tell you what I'll do, Franzl. Because I like you.'

'So tell me.'

'You don't notice that all the champagne maybe ain't really champagne, I'll squeeze in three more somehow.'

'You got a deal, Fritzl,' Franzl said. 'Just make sure I don't get anything but the real thing.'

'It's a pleasure doing business with you, Franzl.'

When Don Rhotten (pronounced 'Row-ten') and Senator J. Ellwood 'Jaws' Fisch could not find the topless desk persons in the lobby of the Bristol Hotel, they were, of course, somewhat disappointed, but not quite at the point of despair.

'Think about it, Don,' Jaws said. 'If you were a topless desk person looking for a little action in a hotel lobby and you couldn't find it, what would you do?'

'Try another hotel?' Don Rhotten replied. 'Gee, Jaws, I'd rather not. It's windy out there, and I'm wearing one of my best rugs.'

'What I meant,' Jaws replied, 'what I would do, if I were a topless desk person in similar circumstances, would be to go to the hotel bar.'

'Good thinking, Jaws,' Don said.

'I'm a senator, you know. You don't get to be a senator unless you learn to stay on top of things.'

'You're a wise man, Jaws. You remind me very much of my pal the Honourable Edwards L. Jackson. Except for the hair, of course. His is silver grey.'

'The Edwards L. Jackson on the House Committee on Sidewalks, Subways and Sewers, that Honourable Edwards Jackson?'

'Right,' Don Rhotten replied. 'He lets his friends, and I am proud to be able to include myself in that noble legion, call him "Smiling Jack".'

'I know him well,' Senator Fisch said.

'Do you really?' Don Rhotten said as they walked into the bar. 'It's a small world, ain't it?'

'A congressman is not quite the same thing as a senator,' Jaws said. 'But they're better than lousy civilians, of course. Present company excepted.'

'No offence taken, Don Rhotten said.

'How did you meet ol' Smiling Jack?'

'I'd rather not get into that, if you don't mind,' Don Rhotten said. He changed the subject. 'There's no topless desk persons in here either,' he said, quickly scanning the bar.

'Well, let's have a little drinky-poo, anyway, since we're here,' the senator said.

'Why not?' Don Rhotten said. 'Maybe if we stick around, one or two of them will show up.'

'I wanted to talk to you anyway, Don,' the senator said. 'About our spontaneous interview.'

'You'll have to talk to Seymour about that, Jaws,' Don Rhotten said. 'He handles that end. I don't like to get messed up with details.'

'I wouldn't think of interfering with your work as a journalist,' the senator said. 'All I was going to was ask you to stand on the right.'

'On the right of what?'

'Of me,' the senator said. 'That way the camera'll get my left profile. My left profile is the better of the two.'

'I'm sure that can be arranged,' Don Rhotten said. 'What the hell, we're pals, aren't we?'

They ordered drinks. The bartender delivered the drinks and a bowl of sugar.

'What's that?' Don Rhotten asked.

'Sugar,' the bartender said.

'I'd rather have pretzels, if it's all the same to you.'

'All we have is sugar,' the bartender said.

'How strange!'

'What's the cord coming out of the bottom of the bowl?'

'That keeps the sugar warm,' the bartender said.

'Of course,' Senator Fisch said. 'I should have known right off.'

'I knew right off,' Don Rhotten said. 'If you had asked me, I could have told you.'

'Drink up, gentlemen,' the bartender said. 'The next two are on the house.'

'You don't say?' the senator and Mr. Rhotten said, in unison, and tossed down their drinks.

206

'Boy, that was some drink!' the senator said. 'You always make them that strong?'

'We try to please,' the bartender said, refilling their glasses.

'You speak English very well,' Don Rhotten said. 'And coming from me, you can take that as a real compliment. I'm Don Rhotten, the famous television newscaster and sage.'

'Thank you very much, sir,' the bartender said. 'It's a great honour and pleasure to meet you.'

'I always make it a point to be nice to the little people,' Don Rhotten said.

'I confine that sort of thing to those who can vote for me,' the senator said. 'One can only spread oneself so thin, I always say.'

'You're the famous Senator Fisch, aren't you?' the bartender asked.

'Why yes, my good man, I am,' the senator replied. 'And I agree, Don, he does speak excellent English. He actually has a good speaking voice. Sounds something like that awful Harley Hazardous, when you come to think of it.'

'Don't be silly, Jaws,' Don Rhotten said. 'What would Harley Hazardous be doing wearing a full beard and tending bar in Vienna, Austria?'

'You're right, of course,' Senator Fisch said.

'So you're the famous Senator J. Ellwood Fisch, Radical-liberal of California, are you?' the bartender said, speaking, the senator thought, a little loudly.

'It is I,' the senator said.

'And this gentleman is Don Rhotten of "Waldo Maldemer and the Evening News with Don Rhotten"?'

'I didn't know we were telecast here,' Don Rhotten said. 'But yes, it is I. In the flesh, so to speak.'

'And what brings you two to Vienna?' the bartender asked. Fisch looked at him a little oddly.

'Something wrong with the sugar?'

'No, why do you ask?'

'You keep bending down over the bowl every time you talk.'

'Just bowing, just bowing,' the bartender said. 'You were telling me what you two were doing here?'

'You mean in Vienna,' Don Rhotten asked, 'or here in the bar?'

'Here in Vienna *and* in the bar,' the bartender asked.

Don Rhotten looked around the bar. There were no other customers except a grey-haired old lady in a trench coat and her caged canary.

'What's that old lady doing with the canary?' Don Rhotten asked.

'She comes in every day about this time and feeds it sugar,' the bartender said.

'What's the whirring noise?' Don Rhotten asked.

'I don't hear any whirring noise,' the bartender said. 'Here you go, Mr. Rhotten. Another little snort on the house.'

'Just between you and me, bartender . . . what did you say your name was?'

'Hans,' the bartender said. 'Hans Schicklegruber.'

'Well, just between you and me and the senator, Hans, we're looking for a little action. Where's the topless broads?'

'Topless broads?' Hans Schicklegruber said.

'You deaf or what?'

'Maybe if you spoke up a little,' Hans said.

'Where's the topless broads?' Don Rhotten practically shouted.

'Is that what you're doing in Vienna, gentlemen?' Hans shouted back. 'Looking for topless broads?'

'Why not?' Senator Fisch replied. 'I like to get my teeth into something different every once in a while.'

'You can drink to that,' Hans said, serving another drink. 'There's only one little problem, gentlemen. Topless broads don't come cheap.'

'Not to worry, Hans,' the senator said grandly. 'Providing they take credit cards.' He handed one to Hans. 'Get us two, charge it to that card, and put a little something on it for yourself.'

'It's kind of dark in here, Senator,' Hans said. 'What does it say on this thing?'

'It's an American Express card,' the senator replied grandly. 'Issued to APPLE for the exclusive use of Senator J. Ellwood Fisch.'

'What's apple?'

'The Association of Pup and Pussy Lovers in Earnest,' the senator replied. 'It's as good as gold.'

'I didn't quite get that, Senator.'

'I said it's an American Express credit card,' the senator shouted, 'issued to Senator J. Ellwood Fisch, that's me. The Association of Pup and Pussy Lovers in Earnest will pay for it.'

'And you want me to get you a couple of topless broads and charge it to this credit card?'

'You got it, Hans,' the senator said.

'*Das ist ein wrap!*' the grey-haired lady suddenly shouted. They turned to look at her. She was running out of the bar with surprising agility for an old lady, pushing the canary cage ahead of her.

'What's that all about?' Senator Fisch said, turning to Hans. He was nowhere in sight.

'Where'd he go?' the senator inquired.

'After the broads, probably,' Don Rhotten said. 'At least he left the bottle.'

'I wonder why he took the sugar bowl?' the senator mused, reaching for the bottle.

CHAPTER NINETEEN

'Snookums,' said the Dowager Duchess of Folkestone to her consort, Mr. Angus MacKenzie, V.C., 'can you ever find it in your heart to forgive me?'

'I'll give it some thought,' Mr. MacKenzie replied, 'and let ye know after a bit.'

'You forgive her, Angus,' Reverend Mother Emeritus Margaret H. W. Wilson said, in the nature of an order. 'Or else!'

'I forgive you,' Angus said grandly.

'It's just that I know how attractive you are to the gentle sex,' the dowager duchess said.

'I am that,' Angus agreed.

'That I thought, perhaps in a moment of weakness . . .'

'With that ugly old woman?' Angus said. 'Now, *that*'s unforgivable.'

'He's got a point there, Hot Lips,' Hawkeye said.

'Shut up, Hawkeye,' Hot Lips said.

'And she did give you two dozen roses,' the duchess went on.

'I told you, Florabelle, and I told you,' Angus said, 'she was throwing them flowers at the dogs!'

'I found it hard to believe that anyone would attempt to harm those harmless puppies,' the duchess said.

'To know the lady is to loathe her,' Trapper John said.

'Until,' the duchess went on, 'Colonel de la Chevaux told me what APPLE does with the money they collect.'

'With what's left over they pay Taylor P. Jambon and the senator their consultant's fees,' Horsey said. 'Gee, I wish we was all back in Louisiana.'

'Why do you say that, Colonel?' the dowager duchess asked. 'Aren't you having a good time here?'

'I'm having a fine time, Florabelle,' Horsey said. 'I was just thinking that if we were all back in Louisiana, and since that Taylor P. Jambon and Senator Fisch like animals so much, I would let them play with a couple of my Louisana alligators.'

'That would constitute cruelty to alligators, Horsey,' Trapper John said.

'But the swamp rat,' Boris said, 'has given me an idea. Since it is my idea, it is naturally a brilliant idea, one which will solve the problem of what to do about all these people. Where's Harley and Trench Coat Wally?'

'Wally's getting his film developed,' Trapper replied.

'And Harley Hazardous is trying to unglue his beard,' Hawkeye said.

'We're not through with that beard,' Boris said. 'Somebody find him and tell him to glue it back on.'

'What's on your mind, Old Bull Bellow?' Hawkeye asked.

'Your Grace,' Boris said, turning to Florabelle. 'Certainly, at some time, someone of your exquisite beauty has entertained thoughts of a career on the boards.'

'Oh, Boris,' Florabelle said, 'that must be the secret of your attraction to women. You can read their innermost secret thoughts!'

'My God!' Boris said. 'I hope not! What I was thinking, sweetie, was that we stage a little drama before the cameras.'

'What kind of a drama?' Angus inquired. 'That's me bride yer talkin' to, Boris. I've seen those home movies you and Doc Yancey make, you know.'

'I hope I'm not interrupting anything?' Trench Coat Wally Michaels said, coming into the suite.

'How's the film?' Hawkeye asked.

'Perfect,' Trench Coat Wally said. 'That's why I'm here. I carried out my part of the bargain, and now the big fella has to carry out his.'

'Throwing Rotten Don into the fountain will have to wait a bit,' Boris said. 'We have need of your cinematographic talent, Trench Coat Wally.'

'A deal's a deal,' Trench Coat Wally said. 'Are you going to throw him into the fountain or not?'

'Of course I will,' Boris said. 'But wait until you hear what else I have in mind.'

Taylor P. Jambon and Seymour G. Schwartz, dressed for the occasion in frock coats, striped pants and the other parts

211

of what is known in upper class circles as formal morning clothing, including silk top hats, walked off the elevator and down the hotel corridor until they came to the ducal suite.

Taylor P. Jambon shined his shoes a final time by rubbing them against the backs of his trousers as Mr. Schwartz knocked at the door.

'May I help you gentlemen?' the man who opened the door said.

'You must be,' Taylor P. Jambon said, bowing, 'His Highness the Duke.'

'One addresses, sir,' the man said, 'a duke as "Your Grace" or "His Grace".'

'Excuse me, His Grace,' Taylor P. Jambon said, confessing, 'I'm a little new at this.'

'I am Theosophilus, the butler, sir,' Dr. Yancey said. 'His Grace is not available at the moment.' (His Grace was, in fact, riding the ferris wheel in the Prater — Vienna's enormous amusement park — in the company of Miss Beverly Chambers, Lieutenant (j.g.) Joanne Pauline Jones, and Richard Wilson, M.D. Dr. Yancey, however, didn't think this was anybody's business and did not elaborate.

'We're here to see the lady with the tame tiger,' Seymour G. Schwartz said. 'A guy named Angus said we was to say he sent us.'

'That would be Her Grace the Dowager Duchess,' Dr. Yancey said. 'If you will follow me, please?'

He turned around and marched into the suite. Taylor P. Jambon and Seymour G. Schwartz marched after him. Theosophilus the butler threw open a set of double doors.

'Two persons to see Her Grace!' he announced.

Seymour G. Schwartz and Taylor P. Jambon could see Her Grace. She looked exactly like what they thought an Her Grace would look like. She was wearing a long white dress, sitting on a throne, covered with what looked like the Crown Jewels of the British Empire, including a tiara resting atop her head. Boris had made a little telephone call to the prop department of the State Opera across the street, and shortly afterwards the throne (from the set of *Richard III*) and the jewels (from *Salome;* the seven veils, Boris said, would not be required) had been delivered. The tiara, however, was real. The duchess would wear it later at the dinner.

'Action! Camera! Roll it!' someone said.

'What was that?' Seymour G. Schwartz said. He was staring at the throne. For the first time he saw two other people by it. One was some sort of an upper-crust nun, he realized, and the other was some sort of a flunky animal tamer. A portly chap with a full beard, he stood over the tiger holding a whip in his hands.

'I thought I heard someone say "Action, camera, roll it!"' Taylor P. Jambon said.

'I was whispering,' the butler said. 'Perhaps you misunderstood me?'

'What did you whisper?'

'I whispered that one approaches Her Grace on one's knees,' Theosophilus said,

'You've got to be kidding,' Taylor P. Jambon said. 'I'm Taylor P. Jambon, the famous gourmet and animal lover. I don't get on my knees!'

'On your knees, stupid,' Seymour said. 'We need that tiger!'

They crossed the room on their knees.

'Good afternoon, Her Grace!' Taylor P. Jambon said.

'You wished to see me, gentlemen?' the dowager duchess asked.

'Not too close to the duchess, Chubby,' the animal tamer said, sticking the whip in front of Seymour's nose.

'Watch it with the whip!' Taylor P. said.

'Her Grace,' Seymour said. 'I'm Seymour G. Schwartz, and this is Mr. Taylor P. Jambon, the famous animal lover and gourmet.'

'I have heard of Mr. Jambon, of course,' the duchess said.

'How would you like to loan us your tiger?' Seymour, who believed in getting right to the point, asked.

'I beg your pardon?'

'In a good cause, Her Grace,' Taylor P. Jambon said sweetly.

'That's Your Grace, stupid,' Hot Lips said.

'Now, now, Reverend Mother,' the duchess said. 'We must

213

be patient with these ignorant colonials. They don't know any better.'

'Your Grace,' Taylor P. Jambon said. 'My friend and I, and America's most beloved thespian, Miss Patience Throck-bottom Worthington, are here in Vienna on a mission of mercy to the world's pups and pussycats.'

'Is that so?' Her Grace inquired.

'That's so,' Seymour G. Schwartz said.

'We are going to make television commercials, appeals, so to speak, for people out there in TV land to open their hearts . . .' Taylor P. said.

'More important,' Seymour said, 'their chequebooks . . .'

'. . . to help starving pups and pussycats.'

'. . . and mistreated kangaroos and other darling, helpless, oppressed animals.'

'Oh,' the duchess said. 'You're from the Society for the Prevention of Cruelty to Animals?'

'Not quite, Your Grace,' Seymour G. Schwartz said.

'Perhaps the American Animal Shelter Society?' the duchess pursued.

'Not exactly,' Taylor P. Jambon confessed.

'This is our own little . . . operation, Your Grace,' Seymour G. Schwartz said, catching himself just in time. He had almost said 'dodge'.

'I see,' the duchess said. 'And what is it you want of me?'

'We would like to borrow your tiger,' Seymour G. Schwartz said. 'We feel that it would really melt the hearts of those out there in TV land if Miss Worthington could make her appeal while stroking that darling cat's head.'

'Miss Worthington likes animals?' the duchess inquired.

'She loves animals, Your Grace,' Seymour G. Schwartz said. 'She was saying to me just the other day, wasn't she, Taylor P., "Seymour, I really love animals." '

'That's exactly what she said,' Taylor P. Jambon agreed.

'How very good of you!' the duchess said, 'You must really be good men!'

'That's just what I was saying, Your Grace,' Taylor P. began, 'the other day. "Seymour," I said, "you're a . . ." '

'Shut up, Taylor P.,' Seymour G. Schwartz said.

214

'Tell me,' the duchess said, 'what happens to the money you collect?'

'Why, we spend it on the animals, of course!' Taylor P. Jambon said.

'All of it?'

'Every dime over necessary expenses, Your Grace,' Seymour said. 'Every dime over expenses.'

'Take it again from "money you collect",' a voice called.

'What was that?' Seymour G. Schwartz said.

The animal trainer shoved the whip closer to his face.

'Jesus, if I didn't know better, I'd swear that was Trench Coat Wally Michael's voice,' Taylor P. Jambon said.

'Tell me,' the duchess repeated, 'what happens to the money you collect?'

'Why, we spend it on the animals, of course,' Taylor P. Jambon repeated.

'All of it?'

'Every dime over necessary expenses, Your Grace,' Seymour said again. 'Every dime over expenses.'

'That's a wrap,' the voice called.

The animal trainer, to Taylor P. Jambon's visible relief, pulled the whip handle back from where it had been right in front of his mouth.

'Reverend Mother,' the duchess said, 'these gentlemen wish to borrow Wee Baby Brother. Would you be good enough to go with them, so that he won't feel lonely?'

'You bet I will,' Reverend Mother said. 'I won't let him out of my sight.'

'Your Grace,' Seymour G. Schwartz, who had no intention of playing nursemaid to a tiger for three seconds more than was absolutely necessary, said, 'we won't need that darling kitty just yet.'

'When will you need him?' the duchess asked.

'We have to make certain arrangements,' Seymour G. Schwartz said. 'We'll get back to you.'

'We'll be waiting,' the duchess said.

As shocking a revelation as this might be to the reader, the cold truth is that Mr. Schwartz had not told the truth, the whole truth and nothing but the truth to the Dowager Duchess of Folkestone *vis-à-vis* the arrangements he had to make.

He had implied that he had to make arrangements for the filming of the APPLE plea, starring Miss Patience Throckbottom Worthington and Wee Baby Brother. Those arrangements were going to pose no problem at all. That would be simply a matter of going to a studio, making up Miss Worthington to look as much like Whistler's Mother as possible, and making the film. They would do that tomorrow.

The arrangements he really had to make concerned the live telecast Don Rhotten would make, via satellite, which would be shown on 'Waldo Maldemer and the Evening News With Don Rhotten.'

This would be because it was live, a one-shot. That is to say, there would be no room for error, because it would be live. There is a six-hour difference between Vienna and New York; when it's midnight in Vienna, it's 6 p.m. in New York.

That meant that the live coverage would have to be shot at the conclusion of the 'Welcome Back to Vienna, Unser Lieber Boris Official Banquet.' That could have posed certain problems, for the singer had a certain reputation for making things difficult for the television media, but the singer's manager (an Arab, for God's sake!) had given his solemn word that the Maestro was personally interested in the good works of APPLE and in Mr. Rhotten personally, and said that Mr. Schwartz could expect absolute co-operation.

If Mr. Schwartz wanted to have the singer, Senator Cacciatore and whoever else Mr. Schwartz might possibly want on the sidewalk in front of the Drei Hussaren Restaurant at exactly midnight, they would be there, at exactly midnight.

The theme of the spontaneous news report was to be that Don Rhotten, relentlessly scouring the world for the news, had discovered that Senator Christopher Columbus Cacciatore; Senator J. Ellwood Fisch; America's most beloved thespian, Miss Patience Throckbottom Worthington;

and Mr. Taylor P. Jambon, famous gourmet and animal lover, were also in Vienna. He would interview them to find out why.

Senator Cacciatore would say that he was in Vienna with Mrs. Cacciatore to go to the opera, where his good friend Boris Alexandrovich Korsky-Rimsakov (who was even more popular among the senator's constituents than Frank Sinatra or Dean Martin) was performing.

Senator Fisch would say that he had come not for the cultural enrichment of the Opera but because he wanted to do what he could to help his favourite charity, APPLE, in all its many good works. That would lead into Mr. Taylor P. Jambon, who would tell all the viewers of 'Waldo Maldemer and the Evening News with Don Rhotten' of Miss Patience Throckbottom Worthington's generous sacrifice of time and talent to make television appeals for APPLE.

And that, of course, would lead into Miss Worthington herself. She would modestly downplay her generosity, saying that she was privileged to do what she could for APPLE.

At the last minute, Seymour had an inspiration.

'Get on the horn, Taylor P.,' he said, 'and tell that nun we'll need the cat outside the restaurant at five minutes to midnight.'

'What for?'

'You're the famous animal lover, aren't you?' Seymour said. 'You're going to have that pussycat on a leash, Taylor P.'

'I am like hell!' Taylor P. said.

'Oh, yes, you are, Chubby,' Seymour G. Schwartz said. 'It'll look great on the tube.'

'You know I can't stand animals,' Taylor P. said.

'We all have to make little sacrifices from time to time.'

'What sacrifices are you making?' Taylor P. countered.

'I'm giving up one whole per cent of the take, aren't I?' Seymour said.

'I'd forgotten about that,' Taylor P. said. 'O.K. Providing the animal trainer is there, too.'

'O.K., you got it,' Seymour G. Schwartz said. 'Get on the horn.'

Taylor P. Jambon reached for it, but before he could touch it, it rang. He recoiled.

'Pick it up and say "hello", dummy,' Seymour G. Schwartz said.

'Hello, dummy,' Taylor P. Jambon said into the telephone. He looked stricken. 'Just a minute,' he said and covered the mouthpiece with his hand. 'It's the Vienna Police,' he said. 'They want to know do we know a Don Rhotten and a Senator Fisch.'

'Give me that,' Seymour G. Schwartz said, grabbing the phone. 'Who is this?'

'Oberinspektor Gruber of the Vice Squad,' the voice said. 'You know a couple of drunks named Don Rhotten and Senator Fisch?'

'Why do you want to know?'

'We got them in the drunk tank,' Herr Oberinspektor said. 'The one with all the teeth wanted us to call the U.S. ambassador, but I didn't want to bother His Excellency with a couple of drunks.'

'You have been hoodwinked, Inspector,' Seymour G. Schwartz said. 'The very idea that J. Ellwood Fisch, a United States senator, and Don Rhotten, America's most beloved television journalist, would be, as you said, intoxicated . . .'

'And chasing girls up and down Kärntnerstrasse,' the oberinspektor added.

'. . . simply is beyond credibility,' Seymour said. 'Whatever the names of your common drunks are, they're not Fisch and Rhotten. Good day to you, sir,' he said huffily and broke the connection with his finger. 'Get me the American ambassador in a hurry,' he said. 'This is an emergency!'

It took a few minutes to get the ambassador on the line. He wasn't at the embassy. He was finally located in the Drei Hussaren Restaurant.

'Mr. Ambassador,' Seymour began, 'we have a little problem. There's apparently been some sort of innocent little misunderstanding.'

'What kind of misunderstanding?'

'The cops have got Senator Fisch and Don Rhotten in the

218

slammer,' Seymour G. Schwartz said. 'I've got to have both of them out and sober by midnight.'

'Those must be the two drunks I saw chasing the hookers up and down Kärntnerstrasse when I came down here. One great big one with a lot of teeth and the other a bald-headed runt. You're not trying to tell me those two lushes were a United States senator and beloved Don Rhotten?'

'I'll meet you at the jail, Mr. Ambassador,' Seymour G. Schwartz said, 'and explain everything there.' He hung up. 'I'm going to get them out of the slammer,' he said. 'You go through the luggage and find another wig for Don.'

In the Drei Hussaren, the ambassador sought out Franz Schubert von und zu Gurkelhausen.

'Franzl,' he said, 'I got a little problem.'

'Problem, schmoblem, if I'm peeling potatoes, you're peeling potatoes.'

'How are your connections with the police?' the ambassador asked.

'I wish I had never heard of Walt Disney World,' the deputy chief of protocol said. 'All this trouble for a lousy ride through the Magic Forest!'

An hour later, after having dropped off Senator Fisch and Mr. Rhotten at the Royal Austro-Hungarian Steam Baths in the custody of several of Vienna's Finest, Mr. Schwartz returned to the Bristol Hotel. He found Mr. Taylor P. Jambon sitting in the lobby talking to four young people. Mr. Jambon was glowing.

'What are you up to, Jambon?' Seymour snapped.

'I was just having the most pleasant chat with these fellow countrymen,' Taylor P. Jambon said.

'Whoopee!' Seymour G. Schwartz said. 'Aren't you going to ask me how things turned out, you-know-where, with you-know-who?'

'Of course,' Taylor P. Jambon said. 'How did everything turn out you-know-where, with you-know-who?'

'O.K.,' Seymour said. 'No thanks to you. Both of them will be here, thoroughly steamed, in time for the you-know-what.'

'Steamed? I thought that was the problem.'

'Soused was the problem, steamed was the cure,' Seymour said.

'You must be Mr. Seymour G. Schwartz,' one of the four young Americans said. He extended his left hand, his right arm being in a cast, to be shaken. 'My name is Dick Wilson, Mr. Schwartz, and as something of a TV news buff, I'm one of your greatest fans.'

'You don't say?' Seymour G. Schwartz said. 'Always pleased to meet my fans.'

'This is Woody,' Taylor P. Jambon said. 'And Beverly and Joanne.'

'How do you do?' Seymour G. Schwartz said.

'We're all fans of yours, Mr. Schwartz,' Beverly said.

'You're a fine-looking group of young people,' Seymour replied.

'Under other circumstances, we would be proud and honoured to buy you a drink,' Dick Wilson said. 'Especially since Miss Jones has just consented to be my bride.'

'Under what other circumstances?' Seymour asked. A little snort, after all he'd gone through, seemed to be a splendid suggestion.

'There are topless females in the bar,' Woody said.

'With really remarkable mammarian development,' Dick Wilson said.

'Dick, darling!' Joanne Pauline Jones, U.S.N., said, icily.

'A professional judgment, darling,' he said.

'The sort of thing innocent young people such as ourselves,' Woody said, 'should not be exposed to.'

'Topless females, huh?' Seymour G. Schwartz said. 'You're right, of course. Mr. Jambon and I will look into the matter.'

'Truly shocking!' Taylor P. Jambon said. 'Well, it was nice chatting with you, but Mr. Schwartz and I must get to the bottom of this.'

Seymour and Taylor P. walked quickly towards the bar. Dick Wilson went to the house phones and gave a room number.

'They just went into the bar,' he said. 'I'd estimate five minutes.'

CHAPTER TWENTY

Four minutes and thirty seconds later, Taylor P. Jambon and Seymour G. Schwartz walked back into the lobby. Each had a female by the arm. The females were not, to split a hair, *actually* topless. One of them, who introduced herself as the Baroness d'Iberville, had, as the nice young man said, a really remarkable mammarian development. It gave every indication that it would momentarily escape from an under-garment visibly under great stress.

The other, who said her name was Esmeralda Hoffenburg and that she was a ballerina, was not so generously endowed, but what she had was concealed only by a blouse with the translucency, say, of a spiderweb.

They were the kind of girls that Taylor P. and Seymour liked. Within thirty seconds of the first timid look exchanged between them, Esmeralda had said that she had always had a weakness for short, stout men, and the baroness had con-fessed that bald men with thick glasses were almost a fetish with her.

By the time the first drink had been served, the ice had been broken, and Esmeralda had said, giving Taylor P. a playful little poke in the ribs, 'I'll bet you're the kind of man who likes home movies, aren't you?'

'Home movies?' Taylor P. said. 'What kind of home movies?'

'You know,' she said, nudging him again.

'Oh, *that* kind of home movies,' Taylor P. said. 'I sure do.'

'What about you, Sy-Baby,' the baroness asked. 'Would you like to come up to our room and see our home movies?'

'Oh, yes,' Seymour G. Schwartz breathed.

'Well, what are we wasting time in here for?' Esmeralda said.

'And afterwards, maybe we can fool around a little,' Taylor P. Jambon said. 'How about that?'

'You devil, you!' the baroness said, jabbing him, this time rather painfully, in the ribs.

Grinning bravely, Taylor P. Jambon staggered out of the bar with her and through the lobby and up in the elevator.

The two couples entered a suite, the blinds of which had been drawn. Taylor P. winked at Seymour. Seymour winked at Taylor P.

'And now, if you boys will excuse us just a minute, we have something we want to show you,' the Baroness said.

'Oh, boy!' Taylor P. Jambon said.

The girls went through a door, and it closed after them.

'Kill the lights, and roll the film!' a voice said.

'There's that voice again,' Taylor P. Jambon said. 'It must be a PA system or something.'

The lights dimmed. The beam of light from a projector flashed on.

'Hey, Seymour,' Taylor P. said. 'Look! It's the senator and Don. They're in the bar downstairs!'

'Shut up, Taylor P.', Seymour said. 'I want to see the movies.'

Five minutes later the lights went on.

'Hi, there, Mr. Jambon,' Hawkeye said. 'Fancy meeting you here!'

'Who is this guy?' Seymour G. Schwartz said.

'His name is Hawkeye,' Trapper John said, 'and he's a doctor.'

'You're kidding!'

'Finest kind,' Hawkeye said. 'But I'll confess. I've always wanted to be a newswriter.'

'A newswriter?' Seymour said, brightening. 'Now, I'm sure that if we just talk this over, we can work something out.'

'Is that what they call an understatement, Hawkeye?' Trapper John asked.

'That's what they call an understatement, Trapper John,' Hawkeye replied. This is what happened:

Twenty-five minutes of 'Waldo Maldemer and the Evening News With Don Rhotten' (that is to say, nine minutes of news and sixteen minutes of what are jovially known as messages) had been aired before Waldo Maldemer faced the camera, jiggled his jowls, looked solemn, and announced.

222

'We have Don Rhotten, our roving foreign correspondent, standing by in Vienna. How's things in Vienna, Don?'

The engineer pushed a button. Don Rhotten, looking somewhat pale and washed out, appeared on a screen behind Waldo Maldemer's head.

'There's a lot of big news from Vienna tonight, Waldo,' Don Rhotten said. 'And here's the big news first: Lieutenant (j.g.) Joanne Pauline Jones, U.S.N., of Wrappinger's Creek, Iowa, announced her engagement tonight to Dr. Richard Wilson, up-and-coming apprentice chest-cutter of Spruce Harbor, Maine.'

There was a round of applause at this, and the cameras gave the viewers a panning shot of a dozen people clapping, stamping their feet and whistling through their teeth. The view showed that they were gathered in what appeared to be a park.

'That really isn't the big news we expected, Don, ho ho!' Waldo Maldemer in New York said.

'I'm getting to that, I'm getting to that,' Don Rhotten said impatiently. 'Senator Christopher Columbus Cacciatore was supposed to be with us tonight,' he went on. 'But events beyond his control won't permit that.'

'What happened to the senator, Don?' Waldo Maldemer asked.

'I wish you hadn't asked that, Waldo,' Don Rhotten said.

'Why not, Don?'

'If you have to know, Waldo, he got in a fight with Senator Fisch.'

'Senator Cacciatore got in a fight with Senator Fisch? How did that happen, Don?'

'Senator Cacciatore found out about APPLE, Waldo,' Don Rhotten said, 'and he punched Senator Fisch for getting him mixed up with it.'

'Senator Christopher Columbus Cacciatore punched Senator Fisch?'

'Right on the end of his nose,' Don Rhotten said. 'He bled all over his boiled shirt.'

'Have you got any more details, Don?'

'So Senator Fisch punched him back. Got him in the eye.

223

That's why he won't come on camera, Waldo. He's got a really first-class shiner.'

'Well,' Waldo said, in his famous fatherly way, 'that's certainly understandable. You said he found out about APPLE. What's APPLE, Don? Have you got that information for our viewers?'

'It's what *was* APPLE, Waldo,' Don Rhotten said. 'It went out of business tonight.'

'Well, that's big news, all right.'

'Mr. Taylor P. Jambon, the famous gourmet and animal lover, announced that he was turning over all the assets to the Society for the Prevention of Cruelty to Animals. And that he was going to turn over all his income from his broadcasts for the next year to SPCA, too.'

'That's certainly generous of Mr. Jambon,' Waldo Maldemer said. 'I wonder why he did that?"

'Don't ask Waldo,' Don Rhotten said. 'Trust me, don't ask.'

'All right, Don,' Waldo said. 'But we seem to be having some confusion, Don. What's the spectacular event'

'What spectacular event, Waldo?'

'Harley Hazardous and Trench Coat Wally Michaels called in before and said there would be something really spectacular tonight from Vienna, Don.'

'They did?' Don Rhotten looked confused. 'I didn't even know they were here.'

'They're there, Don. And they promised us something everybody would love.'

'I wonder what that could be?' Don Rhotten mused.

'Now, big fella!' a voice off camera said.

'You got it!' another voice responded. The next thing the viewers saw, live from Vienna by satellite, was a very large, fully bearded gentleman in perfectly tailored white tie and tails advancing on Don Rhotten from the rear. He grabbed him by the waist, picked him up easily, and held him over his head. Then, with no more effort than a lesser man would expend shooting a basketball, he threw Don Rhotten into the fountain.